Effective speaking
for the technical man

EFFECTIVE SPEAKING
FOR THE TECHNICAL MAN:
practical views and comments

HARRY E. HAND
Professor of English
University of Dayton

VAN NOSTRAND—REINHOLD COMPANY
New York   Toronto
London   Melbourne

VAN NOSTRAND REGIONAL OFFICES: *New York, Chicago, San Francisco*

D. VAN NOSTRAND COMPANY, LTD., *London*

D. VAN NOSTRAND COMPANY (Canada), LTD., *Toronto*

D. VAN NOSTRAND AUSTRALIA PTY. LTD., *Melbourne*

Copyright 1969 © by AMERICAN BOOK COMPANY

Published simultaneously in Canada by
D. VAN NOSTRAND COMPANY (Canada), LTD.

*No reproduction in any form of this book, in whole
or in part (except for brief quotation in critical articles or
reviews), may be made without written authorization
from the publishers.*

Library of Congress Catalog Card No. 69-13335

PRINTED IN THE UNITED STATES OF AMERICA

To technical speakers, those they inform, and all who depend on their skills

Preface

Many scientists, engineers, and technicians spend as much time and effort in the oral communication of technical information as they do in preparing written reports. Yet it often seems that in the training and careers of technical people, little time is devoted to improving the skill of speaking. This book is an attempt to help technical people improve their speaking.

Numerous articles have been written on technical speaking in the last few years, and the ones included in this book present the advice of technical men with wide experience in the art and craft of orally communicating technical information. Their advice is practical and straightforward, but at the same time provocative, stimulating, and rewarding. Most of the authors have actually encountered a specific speaking problem, and each author suggests reasonable solutions which do not always agree with the views expressed in other essays. The views and comments stated may parallel the advice found in speech textbooks, but more often they extend, modify, and apply the familiar prescriptions.

In my own classes I have tried to convince my technical students that the oral communication of technical information is not solely the concern and responsibility of teachers and scholars in speech and communication theory. Technical people themselves are vitally interested in the problems of technical speech, as the articles in this book demonstrate. If students read, discuss, and profit from these articles, then my purpose in compiling the book will have been fulfilled.

Each article is followed by a list of questions (Discussion and Problems) which require the reader not only to recall major points, but also to make his own critical judgments about effective technical speaking. Some of the questions develop speaking assignments based on situations described in the articles. The appendixes at the end of the book provide additional information on technical speaking: a research study concerning manuscript and extemporaneous delivery; a list of useful references; and checklists for the technical speakers and for committee chairmen.

I am grateful to the many publishers, editors, and authors who have so generously released materials and offered advice. Specific acknowledgments are included with each article. I am also indebted to all my students for their prodding questions and interest in technical communication. To my wife Helen and our children, I am grateful for patience and understanding during preparation of the manuscript.

H. E. HAND

University of Dayton
September, 1968

Contents

Preface, vii

Introduction   1
The importance of effective speaking for the technical man—*Harry E. Hand*, 1
Formula for platform poise—*R. J. Norko*, 8

1 The Challenge of Audience   16
Communicating scientific information to varied audiences—*Erwin Di Cyan*, 18
Technical talks for non-technical audiences—*Fred E. Ebel*, 28
Preparing an understandable technical speech—*Lawrence Murphy*, 36
Beware of the expert speech makers—*W. A. Sylvester*, 45
How to address the American Physical Society—*Karl K. Darrow*, 49
The art of talking about science—*Sir Lawrence Bragg*, 62

2 Preparing and Sending the Message   74
Panel discussion: Should a talk be read from a prepared manuscript?—*Arthur V. Loughren*, 76; *Herbert B. Michaelson*, 79; *Gordon I. Robertson*, 82
Candid comment "on reading papers"—*William H. Crew*, 90
So you're going to "read" a paper!—*Harold Haskitt*, 94
How to organize the oral version of a technical paper—*William J. Temple*, 103
The professional presentation of scientific papers—*Harold G. Cassidy*, 112
Some notes on oral communication at scientific meetings—*A. L. Bacharach*, 124
How to master the art of reading speeches—*James F. Bender*, 131

3 Some Important Speaking Situations — 136

How to chair a committee and a technical meeting—*E. J. Tangerman*, 138
Three hard speeches to make—*George McWilliam*, 147
Oral reports to decision makers—*Roswell Atwood*, 158
The modern executive as speechmaker—*Electrical World*, 166

4 Electronic Media: Aids for Seeing and Hearing Technical Data — 174

A complaint about speakers and slides—*Harold G. Lorsch*, 176
Lantern slides and such: How to cope with data and slides—*J. R. Van Pelt*, 181
Slides for technical talks—*O. E. Romig*, 196
Helping an audience to "see" slides—*Edwin W. Still*, 210
How to improve your talk with demonstrations—*Roger C. Wonson*, 218
Microphone technique—*Paul Taylor*, 230
Increasing information exchange at informal meetings—*E. W. Grieshaber*, 239

Appendix A—Manuscript and extemporaneous delivery in communicating information—*Herbert W. Hildebrandt and Walter W. Stevens*, 249

Appendix B—Selected and annotated bibliography of useful information for technical speaking, 257

Appendix C—Checklist for preparing and giving a technical speech, 265

Appendix D—Checklist for planning and conducting a committee conference, 271

Index, 275

INTRODUCTION

The importance of effective speaking for the technical man

Harry E. Hand, editor of this anthology, is Professor of English at the University of Dayton where he teaches courses in English and education. He has published numerous articles concerning technical communication and the humanities.

MANY SPEAKING ROLES

Formal speaking for scientists, engineers, or technicians usually means the presentation of technical information to listeners who are technically knowledgeable to some degree, or to listeners who are at least interested in technical matters. If a technical speaker is fortunate, the audience is both informed and interested in his topic. For instance, an audience might consist of fellow specialists who share the speaker's knowledge and enthusiasm for his field of learning. An audience, however, can represent many possible degrees of technical knowledge and interests: an audience of specialists in another technical field who may not be particularly informed in the speaker's own field and who may have little reason to be interested in his topic; an audience of managers or decision makers who may have limited technical knowledge, but yet need to understand the information in order to make decisions; or an audience of laymen, who may be uninformed about technical matters and uninterested in technical details. In all cases, a technical speaker must face the challenge of explaining his topic so that an audience becomes interested in and understands the technical message which he is trying to communicate.

A technical man must also meet other speaking challenges in his professional life such as chairing a technical panel and meeting, or introducing a speaker to a technical group. Within his own organization or company, he is often asked to be a leader or member of a committee or conference discussing an important development or solving a pressing problem. Or he may be suddenly asked to give a technical briefing to a supervisor concerning a company project. In fact, many engineers present as much technical information in semi-formal and formal speaking situations as they do in written reports.

A technical man may be called on to fulfill any of the roles discussed above, and many others which involve both technical competence *and* speaking competence. As he advances in his career, he discovers that he is often expected to orally communicate technical information to many kinds of audiences and in many different situations. Perhaps the competent technical man advances within his organization and becomes a leader in his own field because he can effectively communicate his technical knowledge and his ideas.

INTEREST IN ORAL COMMUNICATION

Technical publications, organizations, and technical people themselves have shown a strong interest in oral communication. *Applied Science and Technology Index*, a reference guide to technical information, devotes a separate subject heading to "Public Speaking." Professional journals such as *Research/Development, Machine Design, Physics Today, Chemical Engineering*, and *Science* occasionally print articles on oral communication. The Institute of Electrical and Electronic Engineers (IEEE) sponsors a professional group on engineering writing and speech which publishes a semiannual journal called *IEEE Transactions on Engineering Writing and Speech*. The Society of Technical Writers and Publishers (STWP), although mainly interested in writing and graphics, includes papers on oral communication in its publications and proceedings.

There also seems to be an increasing awareness and emphasis on the importance of oral communication among scientists, engineers, and technicians at all levels. Two recent reports dramatically reveal the need and importance of speaking in the professional careers of people from a wide range of technical fields, job responsibilities, and industries. In the Fall of 1962 the Engineering College Administrative Council and the Relations with Industry Divisions of the American Society for Engineering Education formed a joint committee. The purpose of the committee was to find out from engineers who had been on the job several years what needs they had for further training in their professional careers.[1] Engineers were asked to indicate the need for addi-

---

[1] "Education in Industry: Synopsis of the Joint ECAC-RWI Feedback Committee Report." *Journal of Engineering Education*, 55:254-256 (May 1965).

tional training in 123 individual subjects. The committee hoped that the information would be valuable to colleges in determining the adequacy of their present and future courses, and to industry in the planning of training programs. Of the over 7,000 questionnaires sent out to engineers, 56 percent were returned. *Of the 123 subjects listed, public speaking ranked number four; about 60 percent of all the respondents felt a need for further training in public speaking.*

A second report also bears out the importance of oral communication to engineers on the job. Pennsylvania State University recently surveyed by questionnaire the educational needs of 2,090 practicing engineers in Pennsylvania working in 171 industrial and four governmental organizations.[2] Additional group interviews were conducted with 405 engineers in 51 companies. Companies in all industrial categories and of all sizes were represented, and engineers were included from various levels of responsibilities and age groups, excluding those who had graduated within the last five years. One of the principal objectives of the study was to determine the "self-perceived" educational needs of engineers. There was a definite expression of need for further education in oral communication: *77 percent of the engineers expressed a need for "Conference Leadership"; 76 percent expressed a need for "Public Speaking"; and 74 percent expressed a need for "Oral Presentation of Statistical and Technical Reports."* One of the recommendations resulting from the survey was that Pennsylvania State University undertake a larger program in communications for practicing professional people, with emphasis on topics such as the oral presentation of statistical and technical information.

---

[2] Dubin, Samuel S., and H. LeRoy Marlow. *Survey of Continuing Professional Education for Engineers in Pennsylvania.* Continuing Education Office, Pennsylvania State University, 1964.

Clearly, then, the evidence from surveys of engineers themselves indicates that technical people believe that the oral communication of technical information is important in their professional careers.

INCREASING THE EXCHANGE OF INFORMATION

The importance of technical speaking, however, is not limited to the individual technical man working in a job and a profession, or to his own organization or professional group. Competence in technical speaking is important to the whole technical community, and to the democratic fabric and well-being of our nation. Speeches and papers presented at technical meetings, conferences, and symposia may be just as helpful in disseminating and retrieving information as written documents, indexes, and abstracts. The formal presentation and informal discussion of papers is a vital method of exchanging scientific information and stimulating new ideas. The scientific community, speaking through the President's Science Advisory Committee, has emphasized that the ability of scientists and technologists to write *and* speak effective English is a necessary ingredient for improving the flow of information about research.[3] Situations in which people talk and listen are still the most direct means of communicating information and ideas, and the scientific community relies on written *and* oral communication in disseminating and advancing knowledge.

Because of their special knowledge and skills, scientists, engineers, and technologists comprise an elite group which

---

[3] *Science, Government and Information: The Responsibilities of the Technical Community and the Government in the Transfer of Information.* A Report of The President's Science Advisory Committee, The White House, January 10, 1963.

is influencing major military and political decisions such as the uses of outer space. But they also form a group whose responsibility is to inform our citizens about problems with social and economic consequences: automation; conservation of resources; population control; mass transportation; pollution of air and water; new sources of food, fuel, and water; testing of drugs and new products; safety devices; educational methods and media; improving health and hospitals; improving the living standards of emerging nations; and eliminating the causes of war itself. Technical people testify before Congressional committees regarding many of these issues, and the electronic and printed media furnish them a direct line of communication to the public. But unless lawmakers, decision makers, and the public are competently informed by professional people who can communicate information, there will be little or no helpful legislation and action. Our citizens need to be informed so that they can intelligently influence and participate in the decision making processes of a democracy. The responsibility of the technical community starts with knowledge, but in a democratic society it does not end until there is communication of that knowledge to lawmakers and citizens whose lives and welfare depend on that knowledge. The oral communication of technical information, whether it be a speaker to a listener, a speaker to a group or audience, or a speaker facing a television camera, is necessary in a modern technological society that wishes to inform its citizens and to solve its problems democratically.

IMPROVING THE ABILITY TO SPEAK

Despite its need and importance, the oral communication of technical information, or any kind of information, to various listeners in various situations is never an easy task. The effective oral presentation of technical information will always remain a challenge even to the most competent technical speaker. How can he best organize his information for different audiences? Should he read from a manuscript, or should he deliver his message extemporaneously? What, if any, audiovisual aids should he use to reinforce his speaking? These are difficult questions to answer, but every technical speaker or would-be technical speaker must ask them, as well as countless other questions, every time he orally presents a technical message.

The problems are by no means insurmountable. A technical student or an experienced technical person who wants or needs to improve his professional speaking can help himself by listening and observing the ways of successful speakers, by referring to textbooks on the subject, and by reading and discussing the advice of technical men with extensive speaking experience who have written the articles included in this book. Lastly, there is no substitute for the experience of speaking itself. Technical students should take advantage of opportunities to enroll in speech classes where they can benefit from formal criticism and from the discussion of speech principles and problems. Technical men-on-the-job can also enroll in speech classes or in the training programs offered by their own organizations. Every technical man should speak whenever appropriate opportunities arise if he wishes to gain confidence and experience. Only by the process of speaking will he come to appreciate that successful professional speaking is a continual challenge, but one that can be prepared for—and, if well done, one that brings a great deal of satisfaction to the speaker as well as the audience.

Formula for platform poise *

R. J. Norko *is administrator of the industrial engineering division, RCA Electronic Data Processing Division Plant, Palm Beach Gardens, Florida. His experience as manager of training and organizational development at RCA is reflected in the following speech presented before the First National Symposium of the Professional Group on Engineering Writing and Speech, Institute of Electrical and Electronic Engineers, New York, N.Y. October 21-22, 1957.*

YOUR ABILITY TO SPEAK

I am pleased and honored to have been asked to speak at the opening symposium of the Professional Group on Engineering Writing and Speech. Those of your members who were the driving force behind this new professional group are to be congratulated for recognizing the need for such a group, and the rest of you deserve a great big hand for attending and for realizing that there is still something to be learned in the art of communication. The ability to communicate effectively by means of the written or spoken word can make you a more valuable individual to yourself and to those with whom you come in contact each day.

---

* From R. J. Norko, "Formula for Platform Poise," *IRE Transactions on Engineering Writing and Speech,* EWS-1 March 1958), pp. 18-19. Reprinted by permission of IEEE and the author.

In particular, learning to speak before a group can do wonders in developing your poise, courage, and self-confidence. The man who can stand before a group and express and sell his ideas demonstrates leadership abilities. A man who can talk to his associates, co-workers, and supervisors and convince them that his idea is sound and worth trying is the man who is going to get ahead in this world. The man who can speak effectively before groups is more quickly recognized by top management and is more readily followed by those who work for him.

The man who learns to speak before a business group also develops his ability to speak before civic and social groups, thereby increasing his value and prestige in the community. So you have everything to gain and nothing to lose by developing this ability to speak which you have. I want to repeat those last few words, *this ability to speak which you have.*

OBSTACLES TO EFFECTIVE SPEAKING

There are only two things right now that prevent the majority of you from making an effective talk before this or any other group. The first is fear, and the second is lack of experience. Let's look a little more closely at those two reasons. The first one is fear. What is there to fear in the usual audience? Audiences are made up of human beings of the everyday variety—the same kind of people you talk to at lunch, at the drugstore, at the train station. If you are not afraid to talk to them under those circumstances, why should you be frightened of these people when they sit side by side and face you as members of an audience? They are the same people—understanding, sympathetic, reasonable, and not readily given to any violent actions. Why then should you be afraid of them? Speaking before a group is nothing more than enlarged conversation.

The other thing that might prevent you from making a good talk is lack of experience. Of course, you may think the way to overcome lack of experience is to read a good book on public speaking. Right? Of course not! You never learned to drive a car by reading about it. You read first; then you got into the car and tried it. You never learned to play tennis by looking at pictures in a book. You probably watched, listened, and then tried it. None of you ever learned to play golf by reading a book of instructions, and you will never learn to speak before a group by simply reading about it. I am not condemning any of the books on public speaking; there are lots of good ones on the market. But reading by itself will not be enough. The place to learn to speak is on your feet before an audience.

THE FORMULA

I have heard it said that many engineers won't believe a thing unless you can put it into a formula or in the form of an equation. My talk is listed as a "Formula for Platform Poise," and I do have a formula. I don't know whether you could ever prove this formula mathematically, but I can show you people who will vouch for the practicality of it. The formula is

$$P_p = (K_f K_s)^{cde} P' + Re$$

where P_p stands for platform poise, K for knowledge, f for fundamentals of a speech, s for the subject, c for confidence, d for desire, e for enthusiasm, P′ for practice, and Re for repeated experience.

KNOWLEDGE

To repeat, the K stands for knowledge, and the subscript f for the fundamentals of a speech. You are all undoubtedly aware of what the fundamentals of a good speech are. A good speech, like any form of communication, has an opening, a body, and a good summary or closing.

The next part of the formula, K_s, stands for knowledge of the subject. This knowledge of the subject can come simply as the result of having lived through the particular experience you plan to talk about, such as your job, a business trip, a conference you have attended, or perhaps a report on this symposium. On the other hand, your knowledge of the subject may come as the result of research, reading, or study. Whether you have lived through the experience or "researched" the subject, you have a right to talk about it.

Regarding the amount of subject material you need, I can only say the more you have, the better off you will be. The more you know about a subject, the more confident you feel and the more qualified you are to talk about it. Always try to have about ten times as much material as you need; then you can pick and sort through that material until you have the choicest morsels.

I doubt that any of you will ever be called upon to make a lengthy, formal speech at a meeting such as this without knowing long in advance what you are supposed to talk about and how long you should talk. This advance notice will give you time to earn the right to talk about your subject.

CONFIDENCE, DESIRE, ENTHUSIASM

Now we come to the exponent in this equation, which is cde. The superscript c stands for confidence in yourself and your ability to do a good job, d for the desire to tell your audience, and e for enthusiasm. Someone once said, "Nothing good was ever accomplished without enthusiasm." I say and firmly believe that everything is easier with enthusiasm.

Let's take the quantity in the equation, $K_f + K_s$, and raise it to the power of c—your confidence. With your knowledge of the fundamental parts of a good speech and a more than adequate knowledge of the subject, why shouldn't you be confident? You speak the language, you know how long you are supposed to talk, and you know ten times more about the subject than you have time to tell it in. If you think along those lines, you will be confident, and you will do a good job.

Now let's raise this part of the formula to the power of d—your desire to tell the story and to do a good job. With your knowledge of the subject and your confidence in yourself, you can consider yourself to be somewhat of an expert. Try thinking along these lines, but don't give your audience the impression that you are "experting." Just remember that you have some information which should be communicated, that needs to be communicated, and develop your desire to tell your story and to "do yourself proud."

Then let's try raising this part of the formula to the power of e for enthusiasm. The word enthusiasm is derived from two Greek words, *en* and *theos*, which originally meant "god within." Literally, an enthusiastic speaker is one who has a god inside him. Practice being sincerely enthusiastic about what you have to say. Your audience can't be apathetic if you are sincere and enthusiastic. They are bound to begin to think and to communicate back to you to the effect that, "This guy means business; we had better listen." If you are not enthusiastic about your subject, if you are not sincere about the message you are trying to get across, if you are not sold on the idea you are trying to sell, how can you expect your audience to believe you?

PRACTICE

Now back to the formula again. To the part that we have built up, let's add P' for practice. Webster defines the verb "to practice" as "to perform repeatedly in order to acquire skill or training." He defines the noun "practice" as "frequent and repeated exercise in any manner." Notice that there is no memorization mentioned. Please never memorize your speech. If you memorize it word for word, it will sound like it. And if you forget just one word, then you are in for a lot of trouble.

But do go over your talk again and again. Practice it on anyone who will listen. You don't have to make it as formal as a practice session standing before an audience. You can practice it on your wife or anyone else who will listen. Each time you run through it, make a note of those parts that don't seem to go over too well or aren't too clear. Then make the few minor changes that are needed until you are satisfied.

Practicing is an important but frequently grossly neglected part of preparing a talk. The world's greatest musicians, the most famous sports figures, your favorite speakers all find it necessary to practice in order to give a flawless performance. Why should you think you are different? Don't sell the practice factor in this formula short. It is just as important as any other part of the formula.

EXPERIENCE

Finally, to the formula we have developed so far, we add the quantity Re for repeated exposure or repeated experience. Speaking before any group is a lot like diving off the high board at the local YMCA pool. The first time you go off it's rather frightening; the second time it's a little less frightening, and your form gets a little better. Each time after that it's the same thing—less fright and better form. And so it is with speaking before a group. That first time is always a nightmare, but it does get easier each time after that, provided you repeat the experience frequently enough. If you think you can learn to be a diving champion by making a practice dive every twelve months, you will never make it. Similarly, one speaking experience before a group every six or twelve months won't banish the "butterflies" you feel. You must repeat the experience frequently. You must actively seek speaking opportunities. How? Take a more active interest in your social, civic, or professional groups; seek office; seek assignments with these groups. If you have a training manager at your place of employment, talk it over with him and offer your services as a lecturer. How about teaching at a local college, university, or adult educational school? There are many ways in which you can get this repeated exposure, but you will have to go after them yourself.

PLATFORM POISE

That, my friends, completes the right-hand side of the equation. And, as in any good equation, the right side balances and is equal to the left side, which is P$_p$—platform poise. Incidentally, platform poise was once defined for me as the ability to be ill at ease naturally. I can practically guarantee that if you honestly try to fulfill all of the qualifications called for by the right side of the equation, the left side, platform poise, will come naturally.

1 THE CHALLENGE OF AUDIENCE

All speech, written or spoken, is a dead language, until it finds a willing and prepared hearer.
ROBERT LOUIS STEVENSON, *Lay Morals*

Speaking to audiences with different degrees of sophistication, knowledge, background, and interests in technical matters poses challenging if not unique problems for technicians, engineers, and scientists. Although the members of an audience might be interested and even informed about science and technology, they may not always understand a speaker whose life, ideas, and words involve new or unfamiliar concepts, formulas, equations, processes, and mechanisms. Hence, a technical speaker must remember that his message is sent to a listener who is never a mirror image of himself. All of the articles in Part One stress the importance of remembering the audience—how to evaluate the interests and technical knowledge of various audiences, how to talk to non-technical and technical audiences, and how to help an audience understand technical topics. Part One opens with articles offering specific suggestions on how to make technical material comprehensible to various kinds of listeners, and closes with an article stressing the idea that the primary purpose of a talk about science is not so much to convey information as to create a state of mind or a point of view.

Communicating scientific information to varied audiences *

Erwin Di Cyan, who often writes on problems of technical communication, is director of Di Cyan and Brown, Consulting Chemists, New York City. Dr. Di Cyan reminds speakers that the same words and explanations do not necessarily communicate meaning to audiences who may differ in levels of scientific knowledge and experience. A speaker trying to clarify an idea, a mechanism, or process must remember that audiences with varying degrees of sophistication and interests require different approaches.

WORDS AND MEANING

Words themselves convey no meaning nor thought, nor the intention of the speaker. Note the example in the following sentence of simple words: *She was a little grown child crazy us without watercress and bloom.*

The above example of dissociated thinking carries no big words in its framework. Yet it conveys no meaning to its audience. Indeed, the foregoing is an exaggerated example. Yet the one which follows, while it does not carry with it the bizarreness of the above sentence, is not readily understood except by a highly specialized audience: *The personality pattern of the alcoholic borrows the characteristics of lack*

---

* Reprinted from Erwin Di Cyan, "Communication—Its Varied Audiences," *Research/Development Magazine* (September 1960), pp. 30-39, by permission of the publisher and author. Copyright 1967 by F. D. Thompson Publications, Inc.

of self-acceptance with inhibition of aggressive traits which are internalized, and exhibits a severely depressed capacity for identification and love, despite a craving for intense relationships.

The above is a well integrated sentence expressing certain observed personality traits of alcoholics. The audience to whom it would be most comprehensible is psychiatrists or psychiatric workers, preferably of the same school as the author of the sentence. But an audience not fitting those specifications—though a reasonably intelligent one—may be more enlightened by the following paraphrase: *The alcoholic is usually not sold on his image of himself. He tends to suppress his rages and he wants acceptance by others— as exemplified in his desires for warm and emotionally satisfying relationships. Yet his inability to accept his own worth as a person prevents his role in mutual relationships as in love, or otherwise prevents reciprocity in a personal relationship.*

An audience composed of grade school children can be given the same notion in its frame of reference and, though precision suffers somewhat, understanding is enhanced: *The alcoholic person withdraws from people into himself; and what he finds there he does not like either because he is not convinced of his own worth. It is as if he says, "I am no good." It is not that he does not like people—but he just cannot play the game, the give-and-take that is part of any worthwhile human relationship.*

ONE LANGUAGE—THOUSAND MEANINGS

Among the American Indians of North America, there were at least 60 different linguistic stocks—languages as different from each other as Alaskan (also an Indian stock) is from the language of the South African aboriginal tribes. Many had different phonemes. Each different stock was divided into various dialects or more properly languages—which were cognate to each other. These languages of the same stock differed in geographic distribution and their zone of operation was small indeed.

Mutual understanding among stocks was further precluded by the presence of polysynthetic devices, which are compound units functioning as a single thought. Algonkian and Alaskan, for example, are rich in polysynthesis. For example, the idea "you-distract-the-deer-while-I-make-off-with-the-fawn" is an example of polysynthesis. (In a remote fashion, it may be likened to the hieroglyphics of the Egyptians or the ideographs of the Chinese—though these are matters of graphic representation and not of linguistic structure.)

By comparison, the use of one language, say English, should assure adequate communication between speaker and audience or writer or reader. A trenchant expression of Gode, the father of Interlingua, dashes that hope: *I understand you perfectly well but I do not know what you mean*, points out the disparity of understanding among people using the identical language to communicate with each other (Alexander Gode, *The Contribution of Interlingua—Monthly Bulletin of Di Cyan & Brown*. November-December 1957).

THE IMPORTANCE OF THE AUDIENCE

Words in a language are understood by others who speak the same language. But that is only the beginning of the process of conveying thoughts. Words must be forged into a notion to express a point or thought. But no matter how well expressed a thought may be, it must call forth a reaction from an audience. In order to do that, it must be *beamed* to the particular audience to which it is presented.

An audience for our purpose is understood to be the recipient of information, whether that information is disseminated orally, or by the written word. The same unit or topic of information—say for example, the use of nuclear power to heat dwellings—may require communication to people in different professional callings, educational levels, economic or social strata. Because these persons may be employed in industry, teaching, government, technical or administrative tasks, their needs or aspects of interest in a given unit of information will differ. And what is most significant, their frame of reference differs sufficiently to affect the receptivity of the same information.

Also, there has arisen more recently an interest in scientific communication among persons in the administrative, as well as commercial phases of industry. Their interest is based on the need to assess scientific developments for possible application to their own business, or for countering competitive activity. Moreover, as science has come out of the laboratory into the realm of interest of the public, many scientific subjects, which may have been otherwise for the consumption of a scientific audience, are now read by the public.

As specialization makes scientific workers more informed in a *given facet* of their speciality, they become commonly less familiar with other specialities. In fact, interested and intellectually curious laymen are frequently more familiar with a given scientific subject than a scientific worker of another specialty.

AUDIENCE LEVELS

Thus, audiences to whom sicentific communication is directed or who express an active interest in scientific developments, are on several levels:

Academic—teaching personnel
Industrial and Institutional—research personnel and development personnel
Commercial—administrative personnel and sales personnel
Lay—interest and intelligent laymen of various vocations

The governmental level cuts across all levels. Some government institutions, for example, the National Institutes of Health and similar centers, are virtually teaching centers as well as research centers; the research and development activities of various government bureaus or departments frequently reflect the work of industry; administrative personnel in government have duties of organization similar to those of industry; foreign trade attachés are charged with export and trade problems. On the lay level, however, government's role is the one with the greatest variety of ramifications because scientific communications have immense and profound *political* implications.

ADAPTING THE SUBJECT TO THE AUDIENCE

The best illustration of why the same subject and aspect requires different audience treatment, is the communication of a new product development. Laboratory scientists have long known that a memo on a development to laboratory coworkers, is a different thing from a memo to non-technical management on the same subject, and a different thing from a memo to the patent department—though all three memos deal with the identical subject. The reason for the disparity in presentation resides in the differing areas of interest and orientation among laboratory workers, patent attorneys, and management, and the different scopes of the responsibilities and duties among the three classes.

If the audiences in scientific communication are to be considered, one must first determine to *which* of the varied audiences a given scientific communication is addressed. Certainly, audiences differ in interest, background, experience, and ability to assimilate the information—though they may understand it. Gode's phrase is here again applicable: *I understand you perfectly well but I do not know what you mean.*

It is assumed that the writer or speaker proposes to communicate to the audience a subject interesting to it. But that is not enough. The *aspect* of a subject that a speaker discusses must also be within its interest.

You are beyond your audience if you address them beyond their frame of reference. For example, few or almost no natives of the Far East will be able to follow a debate on whether women should be ordained to the ministry or elected to a gubernatorial post. The question is out of the frame of their reference, socially and emotionally, due to the low status women occupy in the Far East. *Audiences retain only what they can weave into the accumulated fund of their knowledge—and can make a part of their knowledge.*

RELATE NEW TO OLD

Yet, information dissemination presupposes that something new is imparted—this is essentially the process of teaching. The newness of the disclosure may be due to the findings of a new *phenomenon*, the disclosure of a new *mechanism*, or a new *explanation* of an old concept. Material that is new can nonetheless be conveyed effectively, if it is compared or otherwise related or associated with the view or belief it displaced, and particularly if the accumulated differences between the two are explained. Then the accumulated knowledge becomes a landmark around which the new disclosure may be oriented and related. The reason for the success of a speaker who says nothing new—and which is at times not even well-said, is because people know what he means—he had just told them something they already knew. This is a standard device of the demagogue, who then adulterates the old brew with skillfully placed innuenda to poison minds painlessly.

It is simple enough to make audience contact when nothing controversial or abrasive is brought to the audience. But a repetition of the tried-and-true pap is too high a premium to pay for audience rapport. For example, a scientist who is also an experienced speaker was asked to address a marketing group on the criteria used by the scientific staff in recommending the introduction of new products. In reviewing the methods used by the audience of the marketing men he was addressing, he pointed out how the probabilities in their criteria were frequently not more reliable as a basis for decision than were astrology charts. The comparison may have been apt, but the example was most unfortunate. The speaker, who should have known better, completely overlooked the fact that people must continue to justify what they are doing even if the effectiveness of the tools of their job is not at the highest caliber. Instead, he should have presented his method and asked the audience to compare it upon reflection with the methods used in its own disciplines. Comparisons or analogies can clarify a proposition, since they bring the new into the frame of reference of the old.

PRINCIPLES OF SCIENTIFIC COMMUNICATION

Scientific communication has as its objective to inform—thus to disseminate and to diffuse knowledge. It is not aimed at prepossessing men's minds. Though the various techniques of disseminating scientific communication differ, there are a number of devices which enhance its dissemination with any audience:

1. *Evaluate the audience:* Do not recite the technical details of your work to a lay or semilay audience. The large, overall, boldly drawn account will transmit a clearer picture of the topic than details in which the audience will be lost.

2. *Evaluate the reason for the communication:* For example, do not read or recite from your paper at a press interview but speak as to a layman. The reason of a press interview is to write an account for the lay press, preferably with a human interest twist.

3. *What is the purpose of your work:* It is well to begin a talk or a paper to any audience, with a statement of the purpose of your work, why it was undertaken, and what was hoped to be proved or disproved.

4. *What does it mean:* It is highly desirable to explain to an audience the significance of the results you obtained —how they differ from the hitherto held belief, why they are more acceptable or applicable, how they add to the sum of knowledge in the field.

5. *Paper or address:* In a paper for publication all facts —quantitative and others—need be given in meticulous

and painstaking detail. But casting fine figures at an audience when addressing it orally—in the form of slides—is a different matter. It is difficult to follow and correlate numbers from an oral address.

The audience gains an appreciation of the significance of a reported work—it can obtain the fine, fractional figures from the author, who should have abstracts ready for distribution when he steps off the podium. Do not read or memorize a paper—give it conversationally—without mumbling. Do not expect an audience lethargic from verbal assaults to follow an intricate subject when intricacy is checkered by mumbled figures.

6. *Abstract, do not telegraph:* It should not be necessary to read the paper before being able to understand the abstract. The reader of an abstract should be able to gain a concise yet accurate view of the thesis of the paper itself. "A new method for improving the yield of methylorum was discussed" is an example of an imprecise statement. The new method should actually be abstracted—that is the reason for the abstract. The abstract should be couched in specific terms: the new method for *improving* the yield may refer to producing a yield of better quality, or it may refer to *increasing* the amout of the yield. When two or more meanings are possible the specific meaning intended should be made clear in the abstract.

Discussion and problems

1 Any effective speaker must consider his audience. Does a speaker talking about a technical topic encounter any special problems concerning his audience—problems different from those encountered by speakers presenting non-technical topics?
2 What facts do you think a speaker on a technical topic should know about his audience? What sources of information can a speaker use beforehand to analyze and evaluate his audience?

3 How does Di Cyan categorize the various audiences whom a speaker might address on a technical subject? As precisely as you can, define and illustrate the possible differences among the audiences.
4 Explain the value of relating a concept, mechanism, or process to something the audience may already know. Are there any dangers in using analogies? Plan a fifteen-minute speech in which you use analogies to explain a concept, mechanism, or process that the audience may know little about. List the analogies that you select, and explain the bases of your selection.
5 What general advice on speaking does the author offer to a speaker who must communicate technical information to an audience? What advice can you offer to a speaker who must communicate technical information to a specific audience that you may know about?
6 In what way might a speaker solve the problem of making a technical speech to a mixed audience (an audience whose members have different backgrounds, education, and interests in technical matters)?
7 Prepare outlines of a twenty-minute speech on nuclear power plants to be given to each of the following groups: a civic group in a community which has been selected as the site for a nuclear power plant; a group of business executives and industrial leaders who are being asked to invest money in nuclear power plants; a group of citizens educated in science who want to understand the operation of nuclear power plants. What differences do you find in the selection, organization, and wording of your material for the different audiences? Finally, develop one of your outlines, and deliver the speech.

Technical talks for non-technical audiences *

Fred E. Ebel, *who works in advertising for Cutler-Hammer, Inc., Milwaukee, Wisconsin, has wide experience in both public relations and technical communications. His advice reflects a concern with speaking to audiences who may not always share the technical knowledge and background of the speaker. The author discusses and illustrates how the technical speaker can stimulate and hold the interest of non-technical audiences by carefully planning and using techniques such as provocative titles, effective opening statements, props, and verbal examples.*

THE CHALLENGE OF A NON-TECHNICAL AUDIENCE

"Say, Bob, the company's having a group of stockholders in for a sort of progress report on our R and D program. Do you think you could whip up something on that high-temperature alloy of yours?"

"You mean—give a talk?"

"Yeah. About 20 minutes. It'll be a non-technical audience, so—well, you know—make it *interesting*."

Imagine yourself in Bob's predicament. How does an engineer inject interest into a talk on jacketing for nuclear fuel elements—especially to a non-technical audience? Two other factors added to Bob's problem—he never was much of a public speaker, and most of the executives of his company would be in the audience.

---

* From Fred E. Ebel, "Tonic for Technical Talks," *Machine Design* (Jan. 21, 1965), pp. 136-139. Reprinted by permission of the publisher and author.

His salvation came in the form of a friend, a professional lecturer, who offered the following suggestions for making a speech that would be listened to.

CREATE A PROVOCATIVE TITLE

The flat, matter-of-fact title can turn listeners away. Recall the times you read a program and remarked to an associate, "Let's pass up this one and have some coffee instead." Ironically, the speech might have been worthwhile, but the title didn't appeal to you.

Bob, for example, wanted to call his speech "Some Recent Developments in High-Temperature Alloys." His friend discouraged him. "Too prosaic," he said, and then suggested, "How about 'The Alloy That Won't Melt'?" Shifting his thinking to this lighter vein, Bob came up with "How To Beat a King-Size Heat Wave."

A commonplace title like "Numerical Control" becomes a livelier "Machining by Numbers." A new technique in cryogenics could be titled "Absolute Zero—Almost!" A plain "Chemical Analysis by X-ray Spectrometry" could be more provocatively titled "Goodbye Wet Chemistry" or, "How to Analyze and Keep Your Sample Too."

It may be argued that a sprightly title is fine for a lay audience but of questionable value for the technical audience. But if accuracy is maintained, what is wrong with imbuing a title with color? A little showmanship can pack the conference hall.

THE IMPORTANCE OF THE OPENING

Essentially, a speech has three parts: opening, body, and close. The opening is by far the most important, because what you say in the beginning will determine whether the listener will stay with you, mentally. His body will remain in the seat, but if the speech is commonplace, his mind will be miles away.

The attention span of the human mind is extremely small when it is bored. Some professional speakers say that attention lasts less than sixty seconds. During this brief period the listener says, in effect: *I'll give this speaker my full attention to see if he's got something to say. If not, I'll turn him off.* Unfortunately, the speaker has no way of knowing when he is being turned off.

How to Open

What, then, constitutes a good opening? Here are a few devices that have proved effective as speech openers:

1. A shocking statement
2. A provocative statement
3. A prop

An example of a shock opener is found in the lecture of a naturalist who holds up a bag and says, "The thing in this bag could be your death—tonight!" He goes on to explain the shocker. "In this bag is the most lethal reptile in North America—the deadly diamond-back rattlesnake!"

A shock opening is not always possible. However, a provocative statement can be used to open almost every speech. For example, Bob opened his speech on high-temperature alloys for cladding nuclear fuel elements like this: "Suppose you were given a small chunk of the sun and were told to use it as the heating element in a furnace. How would you prevent the furnace from melting? The metallurgical engineer must do something like this when he designs cladding for nuclear fuel elements."

Too often an opening moves slowly because it is burdened with obvious facts. Frequently used is the "It's important" type of opening which says nothing. Bob wanted to open with, "High-temperature alloys constitute one of the most important considerations in nuclear reactor design," but his speech counselor objected. "Create a stimulating opening, a dramatic word picture that will bring the listeners to the edge of their seats," he advised. Bob used his engineer's imagination and produced the sun idea.

The prop is a made-to-order interest arouser. It can take many forms—a photograph, a drawing, or an object, such as a machine part. For example, a blow-up of an oscillogram is displayed by the speaker, who says, "How would you like to have an amplifier with a rise time like this? Wouldn't it help a lot in your studies of transients?"

A popular prop used by the nuclear reactor engineer is a small section of a nuclear fuel element. He surprises the audience with this statement: "This small piece of atomic fuel weighs a little over two pounds, yet it is capable of generating the heat equivalent of over 2000 tons of coal!"

HOW TO DEVELOP THE BODY

After you have stimulated interest with a catchy title and have hooked your audience with a provocative opening, you must deliver the meat and potatoes of your speech—the body. This part is simply an orderly procession of facts that explain, enlarge upon, and prove the statements made in the opening.

If a slogan were to be written about the body, it could well be: Stay with the subject. This may seem too obvious.

Yet, time after time in speech classes, the evaluator will say of a speech he is judging, "I didn't get the point you were trying to make."

If the speaker opens with the statement that he intends to show how a silicon-controlled rectifier adjustable-speed drive works, he should do just that. He should resist any temptation to digress and talk about magnetic-amplifier drives or hydraulic drives. The worst form of digression is the telling of irrelevant jokes.

One element of the body that cannot be overemphasized is the use of illustrations. A real pro's speech will be full of verbal illustrations. For instance, "This recalls the time we got a call from Production, asking what we could do about all the cold-solder joints," or "Let me give you an example." If you have any doubts about the power of illustrations—stories, anecdotes, jokes—consult your memory of speeches you have heard. Chances are the ones you remember are those that were illustrated with good stories.

The same logical, step-by-step approach the engineer employs in attacking an engineering project will work just fine for the body of a speech.

HOW TO STOP TALKING

Once you've made all the points pertinent to the objective of the speech, you may be so "warmed up" and your voice may sound so good (to you) that you'd like to go on talking. Don't! Remember that "a good speech has a good beginning and a good ending, both of which are kept very close together."

The conclusion is the wrap-up of your speech. Here, if the speaker is selling something, usually an idea, he must make a call for action. Suppose the speaker has been praising the oscilloscope as a versatile test instrument. He concludes with a brief summary of what the oscilloscope can do, and then makes this call for action: "Doesn't this show the versatility and accuracy of this instrument? Gentlemen, I strongly urge you to consider the oscilloscope as a practical and most useful test instrument for both production quality control and product development."

The logical conclusion of most technical talks will be a brief summary of points mentioned in the body. Brevity is all-important. The listener does not want a re-run of the speech, but he does appreciate brief repetition of your main points, especially if he has been making notes.

Above all, don't let the audience down by concluding with a limp "Well, I guess that's about it, so—thanks!"

Think of the conclusion as a series of steps. After the summarization of each point, you rise a step higher in emotional drive. When you make your last point, you are at the highest point of emotional excitement. So is your audience. Leave them that way!

OUTLINING THE SPEECH

The outline is a "crutch" that is leaned on too heavily by too many speakers. The result is loss of both eye control and vocal variety. Yet it cannot be denied that an outline is useful for very technical talks.

If an outline must be used, make it short, and use key words rather than complete sentences. If complete sentences are used, you'll find yourself repeating them! Use 3 by 5 cards for your short notes. They're less conspicuous; furthermore, they'll discourage the temptation to write long notes.

READING THE SPEECH

Students of public speaking look forward to the assignment titled, "Reading the Speech." It sounds easy—no notes, no worry about choice of words. Just read it. Yet, the read speech is hardest of all. Anyone can read, of course, but not everyone can read and get full attention from his listeners.

Here's what happens when the speaker reads:

1. He loses eye control of his audience.
2. His voice drops into a dull monotone.
3. He speaks too fast and without pauses.

But just as the outline is sometimes necessary, so too is the read speech, especially when the subject matter is highly technical and detailed.

Many professional speakers read speeches that sound as though they are not read. This is relatively simple when you use the techniques they employ so effectively.

Here's how. Double or triple-space the typed script. This makes for quick, at-a-glance reading. Underline words or phrases you want to emphasize. Write in the word "pause" wherever you want your listeners to dwell on a thought. Don't fill the entire page with copy—having to turn to another page automatically introduces a pause. Read the speech over and over. After the second reading, raise your head, and look forward as though addressing an audience. Your eyes, not your head, should move up and down. Observe these pointers, and the audience will praise you by admitting that they had no idea you were reading your speech.

No matter how you deliver your speech, whether with an outline or by reading, following the rules outlined above should help to insure an interesting speech.

Discussion and problems

1 Specifically, how would you define the purpose of Bob's speech? How would you describe the audience? How do the audience levels described in the previous article, "Communicating Scientific Information to Varied Audiences," apply here?
2 Choose a technical topic such as Bob's (high-temperature alloys) and propose four or five different titles for a non-technical audience. Select one title, and explain your basis of selection.
3 The author describes three ways to open a technical speech, and offers examples of each method. Using each of the three methods described, prepare three different introductions to a fifteen-minute technical topic of your own choice. Try any other ways you can think of to open your speech for a non-technical audience. Evaluate all of the methods which you use.
4 The author believes that verbal illustrations are a vital part of the body in a technical speech. What kinds of verbal illustrations do you think appropriate for a non-technical audience? Give examples.
5 Do you agree that "the same logical, step-by-step approach the engineer employs in attacking an engineering project will work just fine for the body of a speech"?
6 In addition to a call to action or a brief summary, how else might a technical speech be ended?
7 How can delivering a speech with an outline result in the "loss of both eye control and vocal variety"? How can these faults be avoided?
8 What does the author mean when he says that "many professional speakers read speeches that sound as though they are not read"? Do you think Bob should have read his spech, or used an outline?

Preparing an understandable technical speech*

Lawrence Murphy's interest in technical communication began in the employ of E. I. du Pont de Nemours & Co., Inc. He is presently Assistant to the Deputy Director, New York Public Library. The author believes that effective technical speeches must be organized for easy comprehension by an audience. Eleven ways are suggested for helping listeners to comprehend technical material.

CONSIDER THE LISTENER

As the speaker steps forward, the audience waits quietly, expectantly. Or does it? Some people are yawning, and there's a slight noise of snoring. The listeners already know that they should have stayed at home.

And yet this meeting is important. The speeches tell about new work; the listeners might develop new ideas of their own, if the speakers were any good.

But even if they were excellent, why not stay away and read printed copies of the speeches? Why suffer in miserable meeting-room seats?

There's no use arguing about the value of the printing press; but a talk does have some advantages over a printed article. Here stands a man telling about work he has done himself; print can't convey interest in his subject as effectively as his own voice (if his talk is any good at all).

---

* Excerpted with permission from Lawrence Murphy, "That Next Talk You Have To Give," *Chemical Engineering* (April 4, 1960), pp. 151-154. Copyright © 1960 by McGraw-Hill, Inc.

And afterwards, the listeners can ask questions. They can discuss the subject with the speaker and with each other. This personal contact is essential; but if it's not there, then certainly the listeners might as well stay home and read the printed version.

To get personal contact, a speaker must always be aware of his listeners. He has to think about them not only while he's speaking, but also while he prepares his speech.

Let's go back to the audience we just left. Something has just happened. Everyone is awake, for the speaker is good; each gesture, each syllable shows his skill.

But then frowns gradually appear as the audience congeals into bewildered incomprehension. When the suffering is over, the listeners go out thinking that they must have sat through a good speech. They wonder, though, what the speaker was talking about, and they're mad at themselves because they don't know.

A GOOD PERFORMANCE

Was it a good speech? No, it was merely a good performance. The well-spoken words had meaning for the speaker and no one else. He made a mess of his subject.

For no matter how well a speech may be delivered, even an audience of specialists won't understand it unless the contents are as clear as possible. Clarity, however, is always a fast-flying ideal; and it is especially hard to catch in a talk, for a speech writer is easily tripped by the difference between written and spoken words.

And there is a difference. Written words, like paintings in a gallery, can be looked at for a long time. And you can go back and look at them whenever you want to. But spoken words, like notes of music at a concert, can be listened to for only a fraction of time. You can't go back and listen to them again. They are here and then gone.

A speech, therefore, must be understood instantly. This alone would be difficult enough; but, in addition, a speech must be understood by using the ears, and most people don't understand technical material as quickly with their ears as they do with their eyes.

To prepare a good speech, therefore, you will need special techniques.

AGAIN AND AGAIN

Considerably more repetition is used in a speech than would be needed in a printed article. Repetition assists memories and emphasizes important information.

And in a speech, connectives such as "therefore" and "however" are sometimes used at the beginning of sentences to emphasize relationships of information. In print, however, two-syllable connectives are usually buried (like the "however" in this sentence) so that the eye will not bog down on structural devices.

The first person "I" is often used to spark a talk. This is done partly to avoid a confusing third person construction such as: "The equipment that was described" (where? by whom?). If overused, "I" does become tiresome, but here and there it can simplify sentences; and it can increase the personal contact needed in a speech.

Today's sentence etiquette, however, forbids this use of the first person in a printed article, a rule that is based more on convention than logic.

There is a difference between writing and speaking; and a good speech, because of its simple sentence structures and its repetitions of the subject matter, can be disappointing when it is put into print. On the other hand, an adequately written article can be incomprehensible when it is read aloud.

HOW TO PREPARE A SPEECH

How does one prepare a good technical speech? Before answering this, let's assume that an engineer is seldom a politician who needs to persuade, nor is he a dramatic actor who needs to arouse emotions.

The engineer is usually a man who provides information; the main requirement of a technical speech is that it be easily understood. This doesn't mean that the speech should be understood by everyone, but it does mean that the speaker should try to make it understood by people who have knowledge and training similar (but not necessarily identical) to his own.

How does one prepare such a speech? Although there is no charted route to the heaven of comprehensibility, the following 11 suggestions have often been used as guides:

1. *Organize the information.* Many technical speeches fail because the speaker merely belches out the facts, hoping that his listeners by themselves will arrange the facts so that they make sense.

But unless you are composing an emotive love letter, each part of your writing should be carefull related to the other parts; a speech must have a definite shape.

Organization begins with a title, which is a simple statement of the subject. This subject is then broken into parts, and these parts are arranged in a step-by-step report. Arrange the steps either according to time, or in accordance with cause and effect.

However, many subjects require other styles of organization. Material may be presented so that it goes from the known to the unknown, or from the near to the far (or the opposite), or from the whole to its parts (or the opposite), or from the problem to its solution.

Whatever the arrangement, the speech at this stage should be a list of summary statements, that is, an outline. This written skeleton is a good check on your own thinking, for there is no better way to see the development of your conclusions.

Once the outline is written, you can develop the speech by merely enlarging upon parts of the outline. This not only saves time, but it also helps you relate the parts of the speech to each other.

And in a talk, this relationship of the parts must be explained and not merely implied.

Tell why you describe the high-pressure equipment. Tell why you talk about viscosity tests. If you do not, it could sound as if you were talking about several subjects at one time, and your listeners probably would give up trying to follow what you are saying.

2. *Tell your listeners the purpose of your speech.* This point usually sounds ridiculous to the speaker. He is so well informed about his subject that he tends to forget that others are not.

People deserve to know why you think your information is worth hearing.

3. *Don't tell them everything.* Do not make the speech a minute description of your subject. It should be more like an abstract than a laboratory notebook. Details should be left for the printed version.

4. *Data are dull.* You can't squeeze many figures into one short talk, so choose only those you really need. Sum-

marize in your own words what the figures say, both those you show and those you don't.

Remember that you are usually just telling people about your work, and you are not trying to prove every tiny detail; leave the complex proof for the printed article, and even there, much information must be taken on faith.

5. *Summarize along the way.* Tell what you are going to talk about; and after each main point summarize briefly what you have just said.

Here again is a device which is needed for good speaking but can be deadly in a written article. Talking requires more summary sentences than writing, because you cannot depend on your listeners to remember or to understand every word you say.

6. *Double check for clarity.* You can increase clarity by repeating a major point in other words, or by comparing one thing with another, or by using examples and illustrations instead of generalities.

7. *Use visual aids to explain what cannot be told by words alone.* Visual material is needed when you talk about numbers, chemical structures, chemical reactions, mathematical derivations, unusual or complicated apparatus, and the flow of materials.

Three-dimensional visual aids such as models are fine for a small conference room, but they're hard to see in a large lecture hall. Slides are the most common visual aids because of their clarity and low cost.

Preparation of good graphs and charts is a complete subject in itself. But if one word could be used as a planning guide it would be simplicity.

Not only is a simple slide easier for the audience to understand, but it's also easier for the speaker to explain.

Visual aids must be worked into the talk, that is, you

must tell your audience exactly why you are showing them a graph—don't depend on a slide title to do this. You will also have to explain each detail of the visual material no matter how obvious it may seem to you, because your audience doesn't have time to study your drawings.

No matter how good your visual aids may be, they are only an accompaniment to your talk. They are never the main show. If you step back and let your slides do all the work, you are likely to leave a confused audience behind you.

8. *Use simple, direct language.* Avoid confusing your audience with this: "The foregoing experiments are favorable indications that the molecules of the compound in the process of being studied did not under these conditions undergo a type of linkage which might be called crosslinking."

Instead, say "There was no evidence of crosslinking."

Practice your speech aloud to yourself. Your speech pattern should sound almost as it does in conversation.

9. *Define words that you think your listeners will not understand.* By defining a word, you can assure yourself that both you and your listeners will be thinking about the same thing.

Individual laboratories, plants, and offices tend to invent their own special names and abbreviations, and it's easy to forget that others will not know what they mean.

A word should be defined at the time you use it. Don't define a list of words at the beginning of your speech and expect your audience to remember the meanings when you finally get around to using them.

10. *Summarize at the end of your speech.* Just as at the beginning you told the audience the purpose of your speech, so at the end give them a short summary of what you said.

11. *Find out about the audience you will be speaking to.* How much do they know about your subject? If they are already well informed, your talk can be compact and short; but if they are not, you will have to use more explanations, definitions, descriptions.

People can be irritated if you speak above their heads, and they are usually insulted if you do the opposite and talk down to them. Fitting a technical speech between these two extremes is difficult.

Discussion and problems

1 In Murphy's opinion what are some of the advantages of a speech over a printed article?
2 Why is repetition important in a speech?
3 How does the author define an engineer? the main requirement of a technical speech?
4 What does the author mean by his statement that a technical speech need not be understood by everyone but that "the speaker should try to make it understood by people who have knowledge and training similar (but not necessarily identical) to his own"? Give examples of audiences with knowledge and training similar (but not necessarily identical) to the training and knowledge of a technical speaker.
5 List and give your own examples of patterns of organization mentioned by the author.
6 "Data are dull," Murphy says, and "choose only those [figures] you really need." On what basis does a technical speaker decide what data to include in his speech?

7 Suggestion 6 lists some methods to increase clarity. Give some specific examples of these methods. Can you think of other ways to increase the clarity of information?

8 Explain what Murphy means when he says, "If you step back and let your slides do all the work, you are likely to leave a confused audience behind you." Do you agree with his statement?

9 Murphy offers eleven suggestions to follow in preparing a technical speech that an audience can understand. Can you think of any other suggestions? In preparing your next technical talk, list any of the eleven sugestions you used and briefly describe how you applied them.

Beware of the expert speech makers *

The previous article, "Preparing an Understandable Technical Speech," brought a rebuttal from **W. A. Sylvester,** *former editor of technical publications for Standard Oil Co., Cleveland, Ohio. Dr. Sylvester argues that comprehensibility and consideration for the audience are not as important as the technical knowledge and superiority of the speaker.*

SELF-RELIANCE

You're an engineer. So sooner or later you will give a technical talk. Whether it's a small talk for members of your company, or a full-dress performance for outsiders, you will do well to be wary of the advice from so-called experts in public speaking.

Sometimes the expert can help. But usually you'll do a far better job if you rely on your training as an engineer.

The expert's advice always sounds fine. It has the ring of virtue. He might tell you to: consider your audience; use simple words; organize your speech logically; avoid details; use effective gestures and voice levels.

This is good advice for the college freshman who tells his classmates "What I Did on My Summer Vacation." It's useless—if not worse—for an engineer. If you're fortunate enough to be a good speaker, great! Go to it!

But the chances are that you have enough problems on your hands with the technical material itself. Let me give you an example.

---

* Excerpted with permission from W. A. Sylvester, "Beware of the Expert Speech Makers," *Chemical Engineering* (August 8, 1960), pp. 143-144. Copyright © 1960, McGraw-Hill, Inc.

THE BOSS WAS RIGHT

An engineer was asked to give a dry run of a speech for his associates before he delivered it outside the company. This engineer broke all the "rules."

He didn't look the audience in the eyes; he had a sing-song delivery and monotonous intonation; his speech was crammed full of hairy, technical details; and his colleagues nearly fell asleep.

Everybody agreed that the speech needed some pepping up; and everybody offered good, sound, traditional advice. Everybody, that is, except one person: the boss. The boss liked it, and the speech wasn't changed, not a single word.

An assertion of the boss's prerogatives? Another example of a man rising to power in spite of a high lard-factor between the ears?

Not in the least. The big surprise was this: The boss was absolutely right. The speech, read as written, received high praise from the few key people outside of the company who really mattered.

BASICALLY AGGRESSIVE

A technical speech is aimed at a specific audience for a specific purpose. Engineers do *not* listen to a speech to be entertained. They don't go to a meeting to see a lively, neon-lighted display of audio-visual aids.

They want to get some data, some experience, some results that they can't get otherwise. Possibly, they want to get some "off-the-record" comments about something that is not yet firmed up enough to go into print.

A technical speech is not meant to be "friendly." Every technical speech is basically aggressive, although people don't like to admit this. The speech, at least tacitly, is an assertion of the speaker's technical experience and superiority.

Criterion of success for a technical talk is not whether people enjoyed it, but whether certain people approved of it. Who? The people who can advance your status in the company, or the ones who have a financial relevance to your employer. Will these people acknowledge your technical competence?

LET THEM YAWN

But suppose people do yawn? Suppose they say: "He knows his stuff, but he just can't put it across."

And if they do . . . so what?

The very people who decry your speech are actually admitting that your speech is really a success because it shows that "you know your stuff."

Now think of the so-called successful speech. You've heard many of them. The audience laughs at the jokes. They pay attention during the performance and they applaud loudly when it is over. The speaker has his ego lifted, but the net results are nil. No reprints, no congratulations from the man's superiors, no professional recognition. Nothing but smiles and oblivion.

Here are my rules for successful speechmaking:

1. Forget your audience; remember your engineering.
2. Use accurate words, not simple ones.
3. Don't organize your speech into logical patterns; organize your technical matters into patterns of technical relevance.

4. Cram your speech full of details, and good ones too.
5. Forget gestures. If your speech is really good, the audience will be taking notes and not looking at you.

And the final, rugged, decisive question is this: In my speech, what have I put that nobody else knows?

Discussion and problems

1. Why does Sylvester believe that an engineer should disregard the advice of expert speech makers?
2. What does Sylvester mean by the "good, sound, traditional advice" that speech makers offer and that technical speakers should forget?
3. In Sylvester's view, who is the audience, or at least the important audience? Is the speaking situation which he describes a typical one?
4. Explain Sylvester's assertion that a technical speech is not meant to be "friendly" but is intended to be aggressive. Do you agree?
5. To what extent do you think that Sylvester is right in his opinion regarding the basic purpose of a technical speech and the criterion of success for a technical talk?
6. Under rules for sucessful speechmaking Sylvester says: "Forget your audience; remember your engineering." Do you think it possible that a technical speaker could do both things in the same speech? Comment on the other rules.
7. Contrast the views expressed by Sylvester and those expressed by Murphy in the previous article. How do they differ in their attitudes toward audience and purpose of a technical talk? Who do you think is more nearly correct in his advice? Give a five-minute impromptu speech explaining your choice. Is it possible to reconcile the two views?

How to address the American Physical Society *

Karl K. Darrow's abilities as a writer and speaker have won him a reputation among physicists for his grace and style. After serving twenty-six years as Secretary of the American Physical Society, he was named Secretary Emeritus. Dr. Darrow has written numerous articles and papers on physics and taught at several universities during his forty-year career as physicist in Bell Telephone Laboratories, New York City. The following article is directed toward physicists, who in addressing other physicists, may forget that their listeners are not necessarily automatic receiving sets with memory tapes of specialized information. Attention to details such as speaking slowly, repeating main points, and defining private language terms is a "must" for any physicist who wishes to make himself understood among his colleagues at professional meetings. Dr. Darrow advocates that an audience of physicists deserves the same consideration as any other group of listeners.

THE STAGE

Consider an actor in a hit show on Broadway, and contrast him with a physicist addressing the American Physical Society. The actor has all the advantages. He is speaking lines written for him by a master of the art of commanding the interest of an audience (remember that we are postulating a hit show). He has a gift for acting, and also a long

---

* From Karl K. Darrow, "How to Address the American Physical Society," *Physics Today* (October 1961), pp. 20-23. Reprinted by permission of the publisher and author.

experience in the art; otherwise he would not be in the cast. Even so, he is not allowed to speak his lines in any way that occurs to him. Every phrase, every inflection, every gesture, even the position that he is to take on the stage, has been tested or even prescribed by a professional director, who does not hesitate to give him mandatory instructions, or even to alter the lines if they seem ineffective.

One might assume that assured of such splendid collaboration, the dramatist would write a play two hours long without a break, and the manager would be content to offer the play in a barn with benches for the seats. This is apparently not the view of those who are experienced in such matters. Ample intermissions are provided, and an act which runs for as much as an hour is sufficiently rare to cause the critics to mention it. Usually the theatre has comfortable chairs and is well ventilated, or even air-conditioned. All this is provided to induce people to come to a play for the apprehension of which, with rare exceptions, no intellectual effort is demanded.

THE PLATFORM

Now consider the physicist. He has thought out his own lines, and is not always proficient in this not altogether easy art. He has little or no training in the art of elocution, and no director has rehearsed him. His subject requires a considerable amount of mental effort on the part of his listeners. The listeners themselves are usually uncomfortable and sometimes acutely so. This may be because the chairs are uncomfortable, or because the room is hot and stuffy, or because the program has already been running for an hour or more without a break; or two or all three of these conditions may exist together. Laurence Olivier or Helen Hayes might well quail at the prospect of having to sway an audience under such conditions. Under these highly unfavorable circumstances, does the physicist strive to put on a reasonable facsimile of Olivier or Hayes? It may be conjectured that frequently he does not, because of the popularity of the saying that when a meeting of the American Physical Society is going on, the members are in the corridors or on the lawn instead of listening to the speakers. People with tickets to *Turandot* are not standing around on the sidewalks outside of the Metropolitan Opera House when the curtain goes up.

Can anything be done to amend this situation? Very little, I am afraid; but the following suggestions point in the right direction.

1. *Speak loudly enough to be heard in the remotest part of the room.* Some people sincerely believe that their voices are too weak to achieve this. No doubt this is sometimes the case, but I venture to believe that most of them are wrong. In my youth I was constantly reproached for speaking too faintly, and I thought that I could not help it; experience proved me wrong. I do not think that I could manage a speech in the Metropolitan Opera House without an amplifier, but a physicist is not likely to be asked to speak in so large a hall, and if he were he could count on the presence of an amplifier. In a hall seating three hundred persons or fewer, the amplifier ought to be unnecessary except in pathological cases. If there is an amplifier, do not expect it to transform a conversational tone into a loud one. It is better to go to the opposite extreme, and pretend to yourself that the microphone is not there, even though you are speaking directly into it.

The trick recommended by those who instruct speakers is to look at and speak to the people in the rear row. This is often made difficult by the fact that some of the prominent people in the audience are sitting in the front rows; this is particularly common in university colloquia. If this situation exists, ignore it. If Niels Bohr is sitting in the front row and Joe Doakes in the rear row, speak to Joe Doakes. Bohr will hear you.

2. *Write out your speech in advance, and commit it to memory.* I have heard only one objection (from the viewpoint of the audience) raised against this procedure, and it seems to me groundless. It has been contended that a written speech is dull and lifeless; the implication is that an unwritten speech glitters with sparkling impromptus. But the presence of a manuscript need not prevent the speaker from substituting a sparkling impromptu for something that he has written; and if the impromptu fails to occur to him, the manuscript is there to carry him along. Of course, it is possible to memorize a speech without writing it out; this is recommended to those who hate to write. It is a fact that a good speech is likely to be looser in texture than a good article. No difficulty will arise from this cause if the speaker remembers that it is a speech that he is writing.

There are some who think that it is better to hear an unprepared physicist groping for what he wants to say than a prepared physicist saying what he wants to say. It would be fascinating to see this theory given a trial by the Royal Festival Ballet, but nobody ever will. For an advanced student of the dance it may be instructive to see a dancer fall on her face, pick herself up, and resume her part in the ballet; but for practically everyone else it is acutely embarrassing.

3. *If you cannot memorize your manuscript, read it aloud.* This bit of advice will probably be resented, for

we have all suffered from dreary speeches poorly read. There is, however, no compelling reason why a manuscript should be poorly read. Lady Macbeth has to read a letter aloud in an early scene of the play; it is one of the high points of the drama. More than forty years ago Ethel Barrymore read a letter aloud in such a way that it is still remembered by elderly playgoers, though the play itself is forgotten. The trouble is largely that most readers glue their eyes to the manuscript for seven-eighths of the time, lifting their eyes from time to time to steal a glance at the audience as though to make sure that it is still there. Reverse the ratio. It is easy to keep your eyes on the audience during seven-eighths of the time and look at the manuscript during the other eighth. For a manuscript which you have composed yourself, it should be extremely easy. Try it and see.

4. *Situate your topic in the general framework of physics at the beginning, and summarize your conclusions at the end.* Even in a ten-minute paper, a minute at the beginning and a minute at the end are not too much to reserve for these purposes. Do not fear to repeat your main points. I shall have more to say on this topic of repetition near the end.

5. *Time yourself.* The members of the American Physical Society are now pretty well trained in the art of giving ten-minute papers, but longer ones are still apt to overrun. This is particularly serious when the closing bell rings when the speaker still has five minutes to go, and these five minutes comprise the conclusions which are the incentive for the paper. The speaker naturally does not want to omit the climax of his speech, and the chairman is seldom ruthless enough to insist.

This is where a manuscript is particularly useful. Timing-marks can be inserted at the end of each page or along the margin, and the speaker (who should constantly be looking at his watch) will then know when he is running behind and will be able to catch up by leaving out relatively dispensable passages. One hundred and thirty words a minute, or say two-and-a-half minutes for a double-spaced typewritten page, is fast enough. In the timing, allow for twenty seconds or thereabouts of silence just after you make each of your difficult points. These gaps will give the audience a chance to think about what you have said; there are no laws requiring a speaker to be talking *all* of the time at his disposal. The difficulty in timing is greatest when the paper involves blackboard work or slides. Rehearsal is necessary in such cases, and is worth the effort.

6. *Aim your discourse toward the average of the audience, not toward the topmost specialists.* Too many young theoretical physicists speak as though they are instructing Oppenheimer; too many band-spectroscopists, as if they were addressing Millikan; too many solid-state physicists, as though the audience consisted of Seitz—and so it goes. This is not quite so flagrant a fault as it was in the days before the meetings of the Society splintered into simultaneous sessions, each attracting its own coterie of specialists; but it is still an error, and anyone who avoids it is doing his bit toward the all-important end of keeping physics from breaking up into a horde of narrow specialties.

There is one specious argument for the procedure which I am deprecating here. The young man may think that the topmost specialist is also the prime job-giver, and therefore is the man whom it is urgent to impress. But in the first place, it seems plausible to suppose that the topmost specialist forms his opinions of the neophytes from their writings and from personal contacts; and in the second place, the job-giver in the audience may be, say, some chairman of a department of physics whose own specialty lies elsewhere, and who is going to assess the young man by his lucidity and not by his profundity. If these entirely reasonable suppositions are correct, the young man is doing himself a disservice by speaking as though he were addressing exclusively those who know more than he.

7. *The problem of the blackboard.* This is one of the toughest of all problems, and here the theatre is of no use. I have never seen a play in which an actor had to write on a blackboard. I think that an actor would write on the blackboard without saying a word, and then turn to the audience and speak. For a physicist the psychological inhibition against doing this is quite invincible, but at least the attempt should occasionally be made. He can at least avoid the tendency to drop the level of the voice while addressing the blackboard. There are, however, two faults at the blackboard which can often be avoided.

One should write his symbols large enough so that they can be read from the back of the room. I hope I never forget the shock which I once experienced when, having finished what I had fondly supposed to be a good lecture, I went to the back of the room and found that nothing I had written could be read beyond the middle rows. Sometimes the speaker finds the blackboards to be much smaller than he had reasonably counted on; in such a case he has to choose between altering his presentation and confining his effectiveness to the people in the nearer rows. Sometimes, of course, either the chalk or the blackboard is impossibly bad; the speaker is then helpless unless he is good enough to revise his plans and do the whole speech without the blackboard. One ought also to write his equations in the order in which he speaks them, instead of putting each in the nearest convenient empty spot and dabbing with the eraser to make more empty spots, so that at the end of the board is littered with incoherent symbols. One should know in advance just how the board will look at every moment during the discourse, and at the end of the talk the board should carry all of the principal equations arranged in logical order. I am afraid that this is a counsel of perfection.*

8. *The problem of slides.* Most people who show slides at all show too many and show them too fast. (I suspect that this is often because the speaker has prepared too long a speech and tries to compensate by racing through the slides.) Rare is the slide which can be properly apprehended in less than thirty seconds, though exceptions do occur. It is impossible to assign a rigid maximum to the number of slides which can be shown effectively. I suggest seven for a ten-minute paper, but I make exception for the cases in which the argument is shown on slides instead of on the blackboard. The one advantage of the blackboard over slides is that the overfast speaker is obliged to slow down as he writes; this advantage can be shared by the slides if the speaker will give them time enough. There is much else excellent advice to be given about slides, but it has all been said by J. R. Van Pelt in the July 1950 issue of the *American Scientist*. This should be required reading for all physicists.†

---

* Author's Footnote—The "vu-graph" and other devices have come in since this paragraph was written, but the blackboard is not likely to vanish.
† Editor's Footnote—J. R. Van Pelt's article from the July 1950 issue of *American Scientist* is reprinted on pp. 181-194.

9. *The problem of "jargon."* Some people ascribe the difficulty of understanding science to what they call the "jargon." This seems to imply that scientists use long technical terms out of perversity, when they could just as well use short familiar words. This is absurd. If I am giving a speech on a subject involving entropy or a synchrocyclotron, less than nothing will be gained if I avoid the word *entropy* or the word *synchrocyclotron* by some cumbrous paraphrase or by some vivacious popular word which does not mean the same thing. Entropy is entropy and a synchrocyclotron is a synchrocyclotron, and there is no synonym for either. On the other hand there is nothing to prevent me from giving a brief definition of either. It does not have to be a complete definition: I may say that entropy is $\int dQ/T$ between certain limits of integration, or that a synchrocyclotron is a cyclotron in which the frequency is modulated so as to overcome the obstacle arising from the change of the mass of the nuclei with their speed. It may be objected that a person who does not know in advance what these words mean is unable to profit by the discourse. This view fails to take account of the fallibility of human memory. The listener may have forgotten what the words mean; he may even be able to recover the meanings during a few seconds of groping, but during these few seconds the speaker will go so far ahead that the gap cannot be closed. I have often observed that the place at which I lost contact with a speaker was the place at which he used a word which made me stop and ponder. It seems worthwhile to avoid such dangers as far as possible.

There is a sense in which physics is afflicted by what may be called jargons, though I should prefer to call them private languages. This is a phenomenon of recent years.

Formerly physicists were few and far between, and one who did not make himself understood to his fellow-physicists a thousand miles away did not make himself understood to anybody. Nowadays many physicists do team work in large groups. In every such group a private language arises, characterized first of all by omissions. Revelant facts and even essential steps in an argument can safely be omitted within the group, because everybody knows them. In addition, the group invents all sorts of abbreviations, nicknames, and pet names for such things as parts of an apparatus, cosmic-ray tracks of various aspects, irregularities in crystal lattices, phenomena of hole-conduction, and even basic concepts of physics. No dictionary contains these terms; they travel by word of mouth, and often they do not travel fast enough. When they are spilled out before a meeting of the Society, disaster may ensue if they are not defined. Facility of travel and interchange of personnel are doing much to retard the development of a Berkeley language, an Oak Ridge language, a Murray Hill language, and the like; but the danger is always with us.

10. *Style.* The concept of style being vague and the teaching of style lying in the province of another profession, I confine myself to two remarks.

Textbooks of style advise the writer, and therefore inferentially the speaker, to strive for a proper proportioning of long words with short, and (what often comes to the same thing) of words of Greek, Latin, or French origin with words of Saxon origin. Now, a scientific article is perforce overloaded with words which are both long and of Greek or Latin origin. This suggests that whenever the speaker has an option, he should choose the short word over the long and the Saxon word over the Greco-Latin. If a sentence contains such words as *ferromagnetism* or *quantization* or *electrodynamics*—not to speak of the atrocious *phenomenological*—it is really amazing how much the sentence will gain in grace and fluency if all the other words are colloquial and short. This policy also tends to bring out the necessary long word in bold relief.

It is said that the style of our forerunners was largely formed by the King James *Bible*, and that the style of our contemporaries is influenced by *The New Yorker*. Neither of these publications can have much influence on those who do not read them. The suggestion is that physicists should not confine their reading to their professional literature. Read novels; read poetry; read essays; read history as written by notable writers; read Winston Churchill; and read Rebecca West—or if you simply will not go beyond the writings of scientists, read the Braggs and Eddington and Jeans and Bertrand Russell. Failure to observe this precept is partly accountable for the fact that it is seldom possible to tell from the style of an article in *The Physical Review* who wrote the article, and for the further fact that scientists who try to write something for the general public so often do it badly.

11. *A suggested experiment.* I have proposed, *inter alia*, that a speaker should speak slowly, define his private-language terms, and repeat his main points. To anyone who deprecates this advice I suggest the following experiment.

Choose an article in *The Physical Review*; let it be in your own field if you will, lest the result of the experiment be too frightful. Sit down in an uncomfortable chair, and read the article—but read it according to the following prescriptions. Read straight through from beginning to end at the rate of 160 to 180 words per minute. Never stop to think over anything not even for five seconds. Never turn back, not even to refresh your memory as to the meaning of a symbol or the form of an equation. Never look at an illustration until you get to the place where it is mentioned in the context; and when you get to that place, look at the illustration for ten or fifteen seconds and never look at it again. If this is not the way that your listeners will apprehend you when you give a paper, you are an outstanding speaker.

Discussion and problems

1. Darrow believes that audiences are often beset by uncomfortable chairs, stuffy rooms, and long sessions, and that speakers, by following eleven suggestions, can at least try to improve a difficult situation. Is this sort of speaking situation peculiar to the American Physical Society and similar groups of scientists? Can you think of other identical speaking situations?
2. Suggestions 2 (write out and memorize the speech) and 3 (read the manuscript if you cannot memorize it) are aimed at the physicist who gropes for what he wants to say because he has not thoroughly prepared his remarks. Darrow adds, however, that the "presence of a manuscript need not prevent the speaker from substituting a sparkling impromptu for something that he has written." Might the extemporaneous delivery of an address from a carefully prepared manuscript, outline, or notes provide both preparedness and the opportunity for impromptus?
3. Suggestion 6 advises the physicist to aim his address, not toward the topmost specialist, but toward the average physicist in the audience. Compare this advice on audience with that in the previous article "Beware of the Expert Speech Maker."
4. What does Darrow mean by jargon or private language? Can you think of examples from your own technical field? Although

called jargon by some people, what kinds of words are not jargon in the author's view? If the scientist must never sacrifice the accuracy of a word for a simpler but perhaps inprecise word, how can he clarify the meaning of a word? When can short and simple words be used?
5 Attend a scientific or professional meeting and listen to the addresses. What seemed to be the reaction of the audience to the different speakers? To what extent did the speakers follow the suggestions offered by Darrow?

The art of talking about science *

Sir Lawrence Bragg recently retired from the directorship of the Royal Institution, London, where he had served as director since 1954. He succeeded Rutherford as Professor of Physics at Manchester in 1919, was Director of the National Physics Laboratory, 1937-1938, and again succeeded Rutherford as Cavendish Professor of Physics at Cambridge in 1938. In 1915 Sir Lawrence and W. H. Bragg were awarded jointly the Nobel Prize for their work on the analysis of crystal structure by X-rays. The following article, adapted from an address delivered December 28, 1966 at the American Association for the Advancement of Science meeting in Washington, D.C., reveals Sir Lawrence's continuing interest in the popular presentation of science. It stresses the importance of arousing and holding the interest of an audience.

THE PURPOSE OF A TALK

I propose to analyze "Talking about Science." How is it best done? Why is it that a subject presented by A is a thrilling account which leaves a deep impression, whereas the very same material presented by B is dull and boring and produces no impression whatever? How should we present our branch of science to fellow scientists who work in quite another field? How can we present our branch of science to those who have little or no background, as if often the case

---

* From Sir Lawrence Bragg, "The Art of Talking About Science," *Science*, Vol. 154 (December 30, 1966), pp. 1613-1616. Copyright 1966 by the American Association for the Advancement of Science. Reprinted by the permission of the publisher and author.

with men of high ability who are important in affairs of state? How can we make the nonscientist understand why its study means so much to us, a passion they sometimes find very difficult to understand? The gap between C. P. Snow's two cultures is not so much due to a lack of understanding as to a lack of desire to understand. There are philistines as regards science as well as regards the arts.

These problems have been brought vividly home to me in a number of ways. I was for many years president of the Physics Solvay Conference. It must be one of the most exclusive of international science gatherings, because only some 20 participants are invited to discuss the subject chosen for the meetings which are held every three years. I have listened for 12 years to all the Friday evening discourses at the Royal Institution, where a broad review of some branch of science is given, and the speakers are both well known in their fields and artists in framing their talks. I talk to many thousands of school pupils every year, and find the nature of their response to be a fascinating study. Recently we have been framing courses for men and women who are new entrants to the Civil Service, and who have had no scientific training. I cannot help but be interested in the basic principles which apply to all talks of this kind.

What is the basic character of a "talk"? I think it can be expressed by saying that its primary object is to create a state of mind, or point of view, not to convey information. I can perhaps illustrate what I mean by dwelling on the vast difference between the spoken and written account. Under the heading "talk," I am not including a course of lectures where students take notes and the lectures follow each other as a composite whole. Nor do I include the "get together" of two or three experts in the same line of research, for which no rules are necessary. I am considering the hour's talk to an audience whose attention one has to retain and whose interest one has to arouse. The written account can also aim at creating a viewpoint, but its main function is to be a storehouse of information. The argument can be meaty and condensed. It can be packed with tables, graphs, and mathematical equations. This is possible because the reader can always pause and digest it at his leisure, going back over parts which he finds to be difficult. The written account has a quality also which I find hard to define. It is as if the writer were giving evidence on oath, and had to justify the accuracy of every word. He must be careful to give references and all due acknowledgements. I do not mean to imply that one can be irresponsible in a talk, but one need not cross all the "t's" and dot all the "i's." In fact, the talk would be spoiled by an attempt to do so.

A talk is therefore different altogether from a "paper." To my mind the governing factor which determines its art form is this: The success of the way in which the subject has been presented is measured by the extent to which the average member of the audience remembers it next day.

This may seem an obvious statement, but if we use this principle as a yardstick to assess a lecture we have listened to, or in planning a lecture of our own, it creates a very significant viewpoint. The value of a lecture is not to be measured by how much one manages to cram into an hour, how much important information has been referred to, or how completely it covers the ground. It is to be measured by how much a listener can tell his wife about it at breakfast next morning, or, if she is not interested, a friend in the morning train. If we honestly put this question to ourselves and think how little we can remember of talks we have heard, it gives us a sense of proportion and of values in planning a lecture and makes us realize that what we say will go over the heads of the audience if we set our sights too high. I would like now to list what I believe to be some of the considerations which apply in planning a talk.

For instance, suppose we ask how many main points can we hope to "get over" in an hour? I think the answer should be "one." If the average member of the audience can remember with interest and enthusiasm one main theme, the lecture has been a great success. I like to compare the composition of a lecture to that of a picture. Of course this is dangerous ground on which to venture, because art experts differ so much among themselves. But in simple terms, is it not held that a picture should have one main center of interest? It may have numerous subsidiary features, but the composition is so cunningly arranged that when the eye falls on these and follows their placing it is subtly led back to the main center of interest and does not fall out of the picture frame. A lecture should be like that. There should be one main theme, and all the subsidiary interesting points, experiments, or demonstrations should be such that they remind the hearer of the theme. As in a picture, so in a lecture, the force of the impression depends upon a ruthless sacrifice of unnecessary detail. I do not mean that a lecture should be like some modern pictures, consisting of an otherwise blank canvas with one button or other object sewn on it at a place which I suppose has enormous aesthetic significance. It can, on the other hand, be richly endowed with exciting details, but they must be of such a kind that the recollection of them inevitably brings the main theme back to mind. In other words, the lecture must "compose" in the sense of having a pattern because it is this pattern which helps so much to impress it on one's memory.

READING

I feel so strongly about the wrongness of reading a lecture that my language may seem immoderate. I think it is a dreadful thing to do, something quite out of keeping with all that a lecture should mean. The spoken word and the written word are quite different arts. Though the reader can pause and go back to a passage he has found difficult, the listener cannot do so and may lose the thread of the argument. It is boring in a written account to be repetitious; it is right in a spoken account to put a key idea in several ways to make sure the audience has grasped the point. When a man writes out his lecture he inevitably writes it as if it were to be read, not heard. The ideas follow each other too fast. It is, of course, far easier for the lecturer to read than for him to "think on his feet" by constructing his sentences on the spot, because he can frame his sentences at his leisure. I realize that many lecturers read their material from a feeling of modesty, thinking they will give a poor rendering if they have no script. While appreciating their reluctance, I am sure they are wrong. I feel that to collect an audience and then read one's material is like inviting a friend to go for a walk and asking him not to mind if you go alongside him in your car. It is easy for the lecturer to deliver well-considered rounded phrases, but the audience has to follow and to think. If someone says, "I dare not talk. I must write it out," I am tempted to ask, "Then why lecture? Why not send a written account to your friends and let them read it comfortably at home, instead of dragging them all out to a lecture hall to listen to your reading the very same thing?"

We come back, it seems to me, to the essential feature of a lecture which justifies bringing the lecturer and his audience together. It is the emotional contact between lecturer and audience. If a lecturer has to find his words as he speaks, he will be automatically restrained from going too fast because he is thinking along with his audience. Every lecturer knows the trick of watching a few sympathetic faces in the audience and of judging (by noting their response) whether he has been successful in making his points or whether he must put things another way. A lecturer who reads is earthbound to his script, but the lecturer who talks can enjoy a wonderful feeling of being airborne and in complete accord with his audience. It is the greatest reward of lecturing.

Just as the troops used to say, "The worst billet is better than the best bivouac," so one is tempted to say in a similarly approximate way, "The worst spoken lecture is better than the best read one." But there are exceptions to all rules. Some very fine lecturers read their lectures, and I have tried to analyze the peculiar quality which makes their performance possible. I think they are the people who so refine and weigh every word and sentence that their beautiful prose almost becomes poetry—it is like a poet reading his verse. Eddington read his lectures marvelously, and on the arts side I have heard most moving read lectures delivered with great dramatic effect. But I think one ought not to venture to read a lecture unless one has these considerable poetic gifts.

THE FIRST TEN MINUTES

A lecture is made or marred in the first 10 minutes. This is the time to establish the foundations, to remind the audience of things they half know already, and to define terms that will be used. Again this seems obvious, but I have listened to so much splendid material lost to the audience because the lecturer failed to realize that it did not know what he was talking about, whereas, if the precious first 10 minutes had been spent on preparation, he would have carried his listeners with him for the rest of the talk.

SLIDES

Lecturers love slides, and in a game of associations the word "lecture" would almost always evoke the reply "slide." But I think we ought to apply to slides the same test, "What will the audience remember?" Some information can only be conveyed as slides, photographs, or records of actual events, such as the movement of a recording instrument, for instance, a seismograph. But slides of graphs or tables of figures are in general out of place in a lecture, or, at any rate, should be used most sparingly, just because the audience has not time to absorb them. If the lecturer wishes to illustrate a point with a graph, it is much better to draw it, or perhaps clamp the component parts on a magnetic board or employ some device of that kind. I remember well the first time I was impressed by this latter device, during a lecture on airflow through turbine blades. The lecturer altered the angle of incidence and the air arrows by shifting the parts on the board. It was far better than a series of slides. It is again a question of tempo—the audience can follow at about the rate one can draw; one is forced to be simple, and the slight expertise of the drawing holds attention. One must constantly think of what will be retained in the audience's memory, not of what can be crammed into the lecture.

EXPERIMENTS

Faraday had much to say about experiments that was very wise. The best experiments are simple and on a large scale, and their workings are obvious to the audience. The worst experiment is the one in which something happens inside a box, and the audience is told that if a pointer moves, the lecturer has very cleverly produced a marvelous effect. Audiences love simple experiments and, strangely enough, it is often the advanced scientist who is most delighted by them. There are tricks too about demonstration. The wrong way is to do the experiment, ask the audience if they noticed this or that, and then explain what this or that meant. The right way is to start by explaining the significance of the effect you are aiming at producing, tell the audience what to look for, and then, after a pause to make sure you have their attention, to bring it off. These tricks are important because they are all part of fixing your message in the minds of the audience; they have the humble but necessary function of the hypo in fixing a photographic exposure.

THE AROUSING OF INTEREST

Here a most important principle comes in which I think of as the "detective story" principle. It is a matter of order. How dull a detective story would be if the writer told you who did it in the first chapter and then gave you the clues. Yet how many lectures do exactly this. One wishes to give the audience the esthetic pleasure of seeing how puzzling phenomena become crystal clear when one has the clue and thinks about them in the right way. So make sure the audience is first puzzled. A friend of mine, a barrister, told me that, when presenting a case to a judge, if he could appear to be fumbling toward a solution and could entice the judge to say "But, Mr. X, isn't the point you are trying to make this or that?" he had as good as won the case. One wants to get the audience into this frame of mind, when they are coaxed to guess for themselves what the answer is. Again I fear I am saying the trite and obvious, but I can assure you I have often sat and groaned at hearing a lecturer murder the most exciting story just by putting things in the wrong order.

We all know the tendency to go to sleep in lectures; how often have I felt ashamed at doing so myself. Though the best lecturer can never entirely escape from producing this effect, there is much that can be done to minimize it. A continuous even delivery is fatal. There is something hypnotic about it which induces sleep (this is another reason why it is so bad to read). Pauses and changes of tempo are essential. Above all, jokes have a marked and enduring effect. The science lecturer is of course greatly helped by his experiments and demonstrations which make useful breaks.

TIMING

Some try to get the timing of a lecture right by, as they say, "running over it beforehand" seeing how long it takes. I am doubtful of the usefulness of this exercise when applied to the lecture as a whole. I prefer to divide it into some half dozen portions, and allocate about ten minutes to each, marking this timing in the margin of my rough notes. One can sometimes fall into a dreadful trap with a subject in which one is a specialist. One thinks "that point will only take a minute or so to explain" and realizes to one's horror in the actual lecture that, having to start from scratch, it takes ten times as long. Of course the way in which each 10-minute section is to be put has to be carefully thought out and its timing roughly estimated. The advantage of dividing the time up in this way is that the pace can be adjusted during the lecture when it is clear that it is going to be too long or (rarely) too short. If time is running short, the part to shorten is the middle where it will be little noticed. The beginning or the end must not be hurried. It is rather like fitting a patterned carpet in a room which is too small for it. If this heroic measure must be adopted, it is much better to cut a strip from the middle of the pattern rather than to cut off an edge. An hour is as much as an audience can stand, and it is most unfortunate when a lecturer has to race through his material at the end and even then runs over the hour.

KINDNESS TO LECTURERS

A lecture is a tour de force and a good and conscientious lecturer is both nervous beforehand and prostrate afterwards. I think there is a great deal to be said for the tradition at the Royal Institution that the lecturer should be immured in a small private room termed "The Lecturer's Room" for at least half an hour before the lecture starts. Tradition has it that this was originally laid down because once a lecturer (actually Wheatstone of Bridge fame) ran away from nervousness just before the lecture started, and so a guard has been placed over the room ever since. In fact, the guard is there not to keep the lecturer in but to keep intruders out. Most if not all lecturers value this quiet time to have a last run over their material and get their minds into the right mood. In particular, if members of the press realized the state of mind of one about to give a lecture, which is much like that of an athlete about to run a race, I am sure they would refrain from tackling him just before the lecture starts, to get, for instance, his views on the atomic bomb. After the lecture he should be at their service and oblige them in any way he can, because he is free to switch his mind off his lecture.

I have emphasized the difference between the spoken and written word. To prepare a talk, and to write an account of it, are two separate tasks and the latter may be much the heavier. I think, therefore, that, when a man is invited to speak, it should be made clear at the same time whether he is to write as well. I know to my cost what a difficult position one is placed in if one discovers, after agreeing to talk, that the heavy labor of writing up the material is also expected. I am sure the task is often imposed unwittingly, under the idea that if a man is talking he will have written what he wants to say, but you will have realized from my remarks about reading that I feel this ought not to be assumed. The most embarrassing thing is to be told that a tape recording will be made, and asked if one would please correct it. It is embarrassing to see a verbatim report with all the remarks recorded literally, and it is generally far less trouble to write it from the beginning than to try to patch the record.

In conclusion, I hope you will realize that the last thing I want is to seem to lay down the law about lecturing. I have spoken so feelingly about the pitfalls because I have so often fallen into them myself. One has to be constantly watchful if they are to be avoided, and even then one does not escape. It is most dangerous to be complacent about a lecture, to think that it will be all right because one knows the stuff and has given a similar talk elsewhere. Every lecture must be approached as if it were a new problem. No pains are too great in the attempt to make a talk successful, and I believe that, given the right treatment, any subject can be made fascinating to any audience.

Discussion and problems

1. In Sir Lawrence's view, what is the primary object of a "talk" or lecture? What is his definition of a talk? What forms of oral communication are excluded from the definition? How does a talk differ from written communication (a "paper")?
2. How does the author measure the success or value of a talk? How is the success of a talk *not* measured?
3. What is the point of the analogy between a talk and a painting?
4. What reasons does Sir Lawrence give for the "wrongness of reading a lecture"? Does he urge all speakers to avoid reading their lectures? Of what value is "emotional contact" between the speaker and the audience?
5. What do you think that Sir Lawrence means by "establish the foundation" in the first ten minutes of a talk?
6. How should a speaker present an experiment or demonstration in which "something happens inside a box"?
7. How does Sir Lawrence's method of timing a lecture insure an adequate beginning and end?
8. How can the order of the lecture, specifically the "detective story principle," help to arouse audience interest? Can you remember any talks which used this principle? Outline a twenty-minute talk in which you use this principle, for example, in the statement, analysis, and solution of a technical or scientific problem.
9. What does Sir Lawrence mean by the statement that "every lecture must be approached as if it were a new problem"?

2 PREPARING AND SENDING THE MESSAGE

Speak clearly, if you speak at all;
Carve every word before you let it fall.
OLIVER WENDELL HOLMES, *A Rhymed Lesson*, l. 408

The authors of the articles in Part One stressed the importance of considering the interests and technical knowledge of an audience. This challenge is only the first task faced by a speaker communicating technical information. There remains the difficult job of organizing technical information and delivering it so that an audience can easily understand the ideas of the speaker, expressed both orally with words and visually with various aids. Knowing a technical topic may be easy enough for a competent technical person, but organizing and delivering a message to a specific audience for a specific purpose and within a specific time limit forces a speaker to be concrete about structuring and wording his information for listeners.

All the authors included in Part Two are concerned with guidelines for organizing and delivering a technical message to listeners. The advice may vary; for example, one author may advocate extemporaneous speaking in one situation, while another may advocate reading from a specially prepared manuscript in another situation. The reader, however, is seldom faced with the necessity of choosing the advice of one author against another, for there is considerable agreement concerning the questions which need to be asked about the organization and delivery of any technical talk, as well as the answers to these questions. The provocative advice offered takes on the pattern of general guidelines which the inexperienced technical speaker needs to ponder and the experienced technical speaker needs to recall.

Panel discussion
—Should a talk be read from a prepared manuscript? *

In what situations, if ever, should an engineer elect to read his technical talk from a prepared manuscript rather than deliver it extemporaneously from prepared notes or an outline? The question is a controversial one with no single easy answer to fit all situations and all speakers. There are, however, enlightened points-of-view and several sets of guidelines that every engineer-speaker needs to consider and weigh for himself. The three opinions represented here, the first by an engineering executive, the second by a technical editor, the third by a public relations manager, were prepared for leisurely oral presentation before the First National Symposium of the Professional Group on Engineering Writing and Speech, Institute of Electrical and Electronic Engineers, New York, N.Y., October 21-22, 1957.

Arthur V. Loughren, the first panelist, is President and Chairman of the Board of Directors, Key Color Studios, Inc., Mineola, N.Y. He is a Fellow of the Institute of Electrical and Electronic Engineers, and the Society of Motion Picture and Television Engineers.

WRITTEN VS. ORAL MANUSCRIPT

Should a talk be read from a prepared manuscript? I say flatly that some talks should be read.

---

* From Arthur V. Loughren, Herbert B. Michaelson, and Gordon I. Robertson, "Panel Discussion—Should a Talk Be Read from a Prepared Manuscript?" *IRE Transactions on Engineering Writing and Speech*, EWS-1 (March 1958), pp. 14-17. Reprinted by permission of IEEE and the authors.

If a talk is to be read, the talk can be no better than the source, and before I try to justify my initial statement, I should like to present some of the rules for composing this "speaker's" manuscript.

A manuscript describing a new technical contribution is usually prepared for written publication. As such, it has a length appropriate to its technical content, and its style is typical of written technical exposition. In these two respects, especially, this manuscript is not for reading!

Why not?

First, because an oral presentation is usually allowed a fixed time interval, and the cramming into such an interval of the entire word content of a paper intended for written publication is almost fatal to effective oral presentation. The cure for this is the preparing of a separate manuscript for oral presentation, containing no more than 100 words per minute available. In deciding how many minutes are available, also, an allowance of about one minute must be made for each slide which is to accompany the presentation.

The author will object, "I cannot possibly do justice to my subject in 1500 words!" But he will do even less justice to it by speaking 2500 words in 15 minutes. The best presentation he can make in 15 minutes will be one in which he has decided in advance exactly what 1500 words he shall use for his presentation.

WRITING THE ORAL MANUSCRIPT

Once the author has recognized the need for a separate manuscript, he now finds himself free to employ the style of oral English rather than written English in preparing the manuscript for his talk. At this point he has made another major improvement in the effectiveness of his presentation.

One more rule: a spoken word is heard only once; a written word may be reread even after one has gone halfway through the paper. Therefore, it is especially important in oral presentation to start by telling what the paper is about, then to present the material of the paper, and to conclude with a summary. The introduction and the summary must be included within the allowed number of words.

And finally, after having prepared a manuscript meeting the criteria I have just suggested, the author should try it aloud at the intended pace, and revise it as needed.

The author may say, "This is an awful lot of trouble to take." He should remember that in the presentation he not only takes 15 minutes of his time, but he takes 15 minutes of the time of each member of the audience, and this is a big amount of man hours and of dollars. If he expects the audience to give this much of its time to him, it is his obligation to prepare properly.

WHEN TO USE THE ORAL MANUSCRIPT

Now that I have set forth my rules for preparing the manuscript for a talk, when should this practice be used? A man's first talk is usually not very good. So let us say that this one should certainly be read. When he has developed a sufficient mastery of his subject and of his own presence before an audience, perhaps he no longer needs this discipline.

One other class of talk which should certainly be read rather than spoken without a manuscript is the class of talk in which the specific words used may have importance beyond the question of informing the audience before the speaker. Political talks, diplomatic talks, and technical talks involving some matter of possible legal significance are examples of this class. Another example is the discussion of how best to define a technical term or a quantity to be measured. Here, the careful and deliberate reading of a statement is likely to be more certain of carrying the intended meaning than any off-the-cuff rephrasing of it.

In conclusion, I feel that the trouble with talks read from a manuscript is that they are read from the wrong manuscript and not fundamentally because talks may not be successfully read.

Herbert B. Michaelson, the second panelist, a Senior Member of the Society of Technical Writers and Publishers and of the Institute of Electrical and Electronic Engineers, is Associate Editor of the IBM Journal of Research and Development.

HAPPILY WEDDED TO A MANUSCRIPT

Reading a technical paper is referred to disdainfully by some engineers as "being *wedded* to a manuscript." Appropriately, my discussion might well be entitled, "How to Be Happy Though Married!"

If the union between speaker and manuscript is a harmonious one, the audience can enjoy a well-presented paper. If, on the other hand, the manuscript turns out to be a ball-and-chain for the speaker, the audience will quickly sense a mechanical, dull presentation. A poorly read paper is not merely boring to those who came to hear it; the sheer ennui is usually evident on the face of the speaker. He assumes a studious squint as he reads word for word. Occasionally he shoots a quick glance at the audience in a brave attempt to give the impression that he is speaking to them. Unless he has carefully prepared his paper for oral delivery, he speaks in a stilted style, full of the formalisms of engineering writing.

If the engineer depends completely and utterly on his manuscript, he may find himself in a most awkward situation. I remember, for example, a meeting of the American Physical Society at which a speaker showed some white-on-black charts on a slide. Unfortunately, the lines on the drawing were too thin, and the particular projector used at the meeting did not give a bright image on the screen. Consequently, the lines on the charts could hardly be seen. The engineer, however, was faithful to his manuscript. When he came to the description of the slide, he read, "Now it can clearly be seen in Fig. 3 . . . ," and, of course, brought down the house.

I believe that a poor extemporaneous speech is worse than a poorly read paper. A speaker who hems and haws, forgets one-third of what he had planned to say, or has to rush through the most important part of his talk in order to finish in time, does not present as much information as the manuscript-reader.

The pros and cons of reading a prepared manuscript vs. giving an extemporaneous talk are, to my mind, rather simple. It is far easier for the average engineer to learn to read effectively than to become an accomplished public speaker. The small percentage of engineers who have the talent and training for public speaking should give their papers extemporaneously.

RULES AND ADVANTAGES OF MANUSCRIPT SPEAKING

For the majority of engineers, I suggest three simple rules to make a talk pleasant for both speaker and audience. First, he should write his paper especially for oral delivery and generally should avoid the tight literary constructions of formal writing. Second, he should speak in well-modulated tones to avoid monotonous delivery. Third, and perhaps most important, he should look at his audience about 90 percent of the time to establish what public speaking instructors call "contact" with his audience. This method of reading requires little practice. I am demonstrating this method now and guide my eyes back to the paper occasionally by running my finger down the right-hand margin as I proceed.

There are several outstanding advantages of reading a technical paper from a prepared manuscript. The most important is that the paper will retain its details and will keep its correct emphasis and balance, as originally written. Even the best speaker will occasionally forget a point he had intended to make or will be carried away on an unexpected tangent in the middle of his speech. He need not trust his memory if he has the manuscript in front of him, and his ideas, as worked out on paper, will retain their integrity during his talk. On the other hand, if the speaker finds it necessary to make a brief, impromptu diversion, he can later return to his manuscript.

There is certainly no clear-cut relationship among good engineering work, good writing ability, and good speaking ability. We all know engineers who are exceptionally competent in their special fields of work but are either poor writers or poor speakers. In writing their papers, they may receive help from colleagues and from editors or technical writers. Eventually, they acquire a more or less polished manuscript. Acquiring a polish in extemporaneous speaking, however, is far more difficult.

To sum up, then, we will usually save an engineer's time and effort by recommending that he use a prepared manuscript. To become a good extemporaneous speaker, he must, by repeated practice, develop a whole new set of platform habits according to the usual list of instructions: assume a natural posture; don't stand stiffly in one place; use gestures for your more important points; don't talk to the blackboard; speak from a prepared outline or use mnemonic devices; don't say "uh" to reflect a pause in your thinking; time your talk carefully; discuss your slides in proper order; et cetera.

To give a good presentation from a prepared manuscript, he need concentrate on only three simple instructions: write your manuscript in *oral l*anguage, avoid a monotone, and make a consistent effort to look at your audience.

Gordon I. Robertson, the third panelist, was former head of the Bell Laboratories Lecture Aid Department. As Public Relations Manager at Bell Laboratories, his present responsibilities include the production of Bell Laboratories publications and exhibits.

EVIDENCE AGAINST READING A TALK

Immediately after I had agreed to participate on this panel, I found myself in a peculiar position. I had been giving talks—tchnical and otherwise—for over fifteen years and had always instinctively felt that lectures should never be read. Actually, my feeling wasn't entirely intuitive, as all my experience seemed to verify it. But, for the first time, I had to come up with specific, concrete reasons.

So, I did quite a bit of looking back over the years. I also backed up my retrospection with a lot of research and correspondence with the people who study these things. Let me say right now that I found nothing to change my mind one bit. In fact, I learned several things that convinced me all the more.

For example: I contacted Dr. Irwin of the University of Wisconsin's Speech Department. The call was a timely one because Dr. Irwin had recently completed correlating the results of a survey on just this subject. Here's what he found:

Last November, twelve engineers were invited to speak before the school's 66 senior electrical engineering students. All twelve men were asked to ad-lib their talks. However, one old hand was convinced he could do just as good a job by reading his paper. When the talks ended, the students were asked to fill out questionnaires grading the speakers. As it turned out, the man who read his paper came out low man on the totem pole.

Now, that was only one survey—and on a comparatively small scale. But Professor Burton of the State University of Iowa has conducted similar investigations with much larger groups of engineering students and with a greater number of speakers. Here's what he found:

When asked what they *disliked* about the speaker, many students replied that, "He read his lecture." When asked what they *liked* about the speaker, many students said they liked the fact that he *hadn't* read his lecture. And, when asked for suggestions on how to give a good talk, many students replied—you guessed it—"Don't read it!"

Well, I came across other surveys on the same question, but there is no point in itemizing them because the results were identical: Reading a lecture almost automatically puts the speaker way down on the popularity scale.

DISADVANTAGES OF READING A TALK

However, though I was now more than ever convinced of this, I still lacked concrete reasons for its being so. Here's where the "looking back" came in.

To begin with, I asked myself, "Why do people give talks in the first place?" And the answer, of course, was, "To pass on information to other people." Yet, apparently, when talks are read, the information transmission belt breaks down. Why? Well, the surveys made it clear that it is difficult to get information across without interesting your audience—that, in fact, a dull presentation can so antagonize an audience as to completely cut off communications.

Again, I asked myself, why? And here are some of the reasons I came up with: first, few people can read well. The deceptively easy fluency of radio announcers has only been acquired through long years of intensive practice. Engineers and other technical people haven't the time to spend on such practice. Also, any voice shortcomings of the reader will be greatly magnified during the course of a full-length talk, while the personality of nonreading speaker will usually compensate for such defects.

Besides, as most of us realize, *written* and *spoken* English are really two different languages. In writing—even when writing specifically for a talk—there is always a tendency to be over-formal. When such a paper is read verbatim, it will usually sound dull, even pompous. Your words are apt to be like the Redwoods: tall and stately, yet bearing no fruit.

The free-wheeling speaker, on the other hand, is going to tell his story, no matter how technical, in his own words, or conversationally. Few of us have had any training in reading aloud, but all of us have been practicing conversation most of our lives.

Keep in mind, too, that technical talks, particularly for engineering societies such as this one, are usually published. Your audience has access to the printed version and therefore has every right to expect more than a dull, verbatim reading of the exact same material. In such cases, some people even become quite offended.

Just last week, a Bell Labs. friend of mine witnessed a perfect example of this. He was sitting in at a high-level missile discussion that took place shortly after the Sputnik headlines broke. Midway through the proceedings, a VIP in the missile field got up and began reading a talk. Before he'd read very far, a four-star general interrupted. "I learned to read at the age of seven," he said, "and I didn't come here to be read to." With this, he stood up, coldly requested the missile man to send him a copy of the talk, and walked out.

ADVANTAGES OF NOT READING A TALK

So much for the disadvantages of reading a talk. Now, let's take a quick look at some of the advantages gained by *not* reading. I'll sum up the greatest of these in one word: Flexibility.

Some time ago, I was scheduled to give a 40-minute lecture on microwave phenomena. As I sat waiting to be introduced, I was pretty complacent about the whole thing. It was a fairly complex subject, but my material had been pretty thoroughly prepared, and I had 40 minutes in which to get it across. I was pretty complacent, that is, until the program chairman whispered in my ear that my time had been cut to 20 minutes. There I was, all set for a crowded 40 minutes, and boom, my time was cut in half.

Well, I shaved a little here; cut a little there; skipped through some of the less interesting demonstrations; and, to make a long story short, finished up in time.

If I had been chained to a written script, I would have been in real trouble. As it was, I was able to ad-lib an editing job on my talk, something nearly impossible to do when reading a lecture.

It's true this case was a little on the extreme side, but that old devil of the lecturer, "unforeseen circumstances," does pop up often enough.

The point is that the advantages of flexibility apply to any talk provided the lecturer isn't chained to his paper. If he doesn't read, the speaker can use blackboard work very effectively. He can use lecture aids, demonstrations, and charts. He can watch his audience, know when he is not being understood, and dwell a little longer on such material. Or he can spot the signs of restlessness that mean he is staying too long with a boring item. In short, he can adjust his pace to the material at hand, making the most of highlights and speeding through the dull spots. And, because he's looking at his audience, he can make them feel the talk is directed to them personally. This direct contact is more important than it seems. As Emerson put it, "There is no eloquence without a man behind it." If this weren't so, lecturers could just as well send in recordings and remain at home themselves. Which, I imagine, is what the general must have felt.

There are many other examples, but time doesn't permit covering them all.

REASONS FOR GIVING A TALK

However, I think it's necessary that I touch briefly on another important reason for giving a talk. I've mentioned passing on information, and it's the major reason beyond any doubt. But, when you find yourself in front of an audience, you are usually there for another reason as well. You are there to represent your company. How well you do this depends entirely upon how well you represent yourself, and there is no better way of doing this than by giving a good lecture. The previously mentioned surveys make it clear that reading a paper is not the way to do this, no matter how technically competent the paper is.

On the other hand, the speaker who doesn't bury his nose in a paper as if he'd be lost without it is demonstrating his competence by that very fact. By ad-libbing from notes, or from pure memory, he is proving his ability to think on his feet. In short, he is proving his complete command of the subject.

Now, I may have taken up more of your time than I should. But, before concluding, I would like to give you a graphic example of one of the advantages a nonreading speaker has—lecture aids.

With all the new advances in the field of electronic computers and data transmission, we at the Bell Labs. have been called upon more and more to lecture on automation, a highly technical and very difficult subject to get across with words alone. So, we've come up with a device to demonstrate the ultimate in automation—and also, by the way, to get our lecturers off stage when they've run over their time. *(At this point, Mr. Robertson switched on the above-mentioned lecture aid. It is an innocent looking black box which appears to house only some ordinary electronic equipment. Two simple dials and a toggle switch set onto the front panel help to further this innocuous appearance. However, when the switch was turned on, the lid lifted slowly, a disembodied hand reached eerily from within the box, turned the switch off, and withdrew from sight again. The lid closed down over the hand, and the show was over.)*

Discussion and problems

1. In Loughren's view what is the source of trouble in reading from a manuscript?
2. What rules does he offer for preparing a manuscript that is to be read?
3. Under what circumstances does Loughren believe that a manuscript should be used for a talk? Do you agree?
4. What are Michaelson's objections to the extemporaneous delivery of technical talks? Do you agree that an engineer who wants to be a good extemporaneous speaker must "develop a whole new set of platform habits"?
5. What are Michaelson's three rules for successful manuscript speaking? What advantages does he list for reading a manuscript?
6. What sort of speaking situation and audience does Robertson use as evidence against manuscript speaking? He refers to good speakers as those who ad-lib their talks. What does he mean by ad-libbing?
7. Summarize Robertson's view of the disadvantages in reading a talk and the advantages in *not* reading a talk. How do his views differ from Loughren's and Michaelson's?
8. What other reasons, in addition to passing on information, does Robertson list for giving a talk? Robertson says that the speaker who speaks on his feet "is proving his command of the subject." Michaelson states, however, that "we all know engineers who are exceptionally competent in their special fields of work but are either poor writers or poor speakers," and that acquiring polish in extemporaneous speaking is most difficult. Do you believe that there is a correlation between technical competence or being in comand of a subject *and* ability to speak on your feet extemporaneously?
9. After reading the three views presented, what conclusions of your own have you reached concerning the question of talking vs. reading from a prepared manuscript? To what extent might the answer depend on the topic? on the situation or the occasion? on the audience?
10. Read the research study reprinted in Appendix A of this volume ("Manuscript and Extemporaneous Delivery in Communicating

Information" by Herbert W. Hildebrandt and Walter W. Stevens). How does success in communicating information seem to be related to an experienced speaker's ability in using a particular method of delivery? Considering all of the views you have now read, can you arrive at some general guidelines for deciding which form of delivery to use? Under what circumstances would you advise extemporaneous delivery? reading a manuscript?

11 Prepare a fifteen-minute technical talk for extemporaneous delivery. From your outline and notes, next prepare a manuscript to be read. Lastly, prepare the manuscript for publication. Describe the differences between the three versions. Describe circumstances (1) in which you might extemporaneously deliver the talk from an outline and notes; (2) read a manuscript designed for listening.

Candid comment "on reading papers" *

William H. Crew, author of the frank and open letter reprinted below, recently retired as Assistant Director for Scientific Personnel, Los Alamos Scientific Laboratory. He has been active in teaching and research for both academic and governmental institutions. Dr. Crew's letter registers a complaint against speakers who had read word for word from manuscripts at an annual meeting of the American Society for Engineering Education. The next reprinted article, "So You're Going to 'Read' a Paper," represents an attempt by ASEE to improve the 'reading' of papers at its annual meetings.

Dean W. L. Everitt
College of Engineering
University of Illinois,
Urbana, Illinois

Dear Dean Everitt:

I hope you will not consider it unduly presumptuous of me to address you, the incoming President of the ASEE, on one aspect of the conduct of the ASEE Annual Meeting. My comments, which embody a suggestion, took root from my observations at the recent meeting at Ames, Iowa—an occasion which was made highly delightful by the effective local

---

* From William H. Crew, "Candid Comment 'On Reading Papers'," *Journal of Engineering Education* (September 1956), pp. 23-24. Reprinted by permission of ASEE and the author.

arrangements of our amiable hosts and by a commendable restraint on the part of the weatherman.

My suggestion is that members of our Society raise the scholarly tone of the programs by presenting their papers orally *without reading from a manuscript.* Quite frankly, I was aghast to note at Ames the very considerable number of papers that were *read*—I mean read *word for word from copy.* This struck me as distinctly out-of-character for college teachers (of all people!). After listening to a "read" speech, I scrambled, along with the rest of the audience, to obtain a mimeographed copy of the talk just delivered. But why?

I think the answer is the "read" talk fails to grip the undivided attention of the listener. It lacks vitality because it does not carry the spontaneous enthusiasm of the speaker. Therefore we pick up a copy of the speech to read on the train going home so that we can tell our colleagues what the man said!

My philosophy runs as follows. If a man has a message to deliver, the subject must be of interest to himself, and he should know a great deal about it. If these criteria are fulfilled, then let him get up and say what he has to say in the words at his command and audience interest will just naturally follow. Mind you, I think the speaker should give careful and prior consideration to the contents of his talk; and he should plan to present his ideas in an order which makes them easily understood by his audience. An inexperienced speaker feels an inward urge to write out his talk and then read it to the audience, knowing he can wrap up his thoughts in orderly, longer, and more erudite-sounding sentences. The trouble is that the more erudite the sound of a talk, the less intelligible it may be to the listener. The substance becomes confused by the form.

I wish also to make the point that a lecture which is being prepared for publication should, in my opinion, be phrased in language which differs from that used in presenting it orally. Therefore the reading word for word from a manuscript which is to be distributed suffers from inconsistency. Either the oral presentation or the printed version is unnaturally phrased.

Personally, I attend these meetings to see and hear *the man*. If he is going to read and distribute his talk, then I would much prefer to read it myself in the comfort of an easy chair in my own quiet and air-conditioned parlor. But if the speaker is going to talk from his heart on a subject which is dear to himself, then let me hear him under any conditions of discomfort so that I may absorb from him and share with him his enthusiasm.

Finally, there is the man who says "I haven't time to 'learn' my speech; I'll just have to read it." To this, I say he should be mindful that perhaps the audience hasn't the time to listen to what might better be read in print. Perhaps he should, if he is too busy, decline the invitation to talk.

If you, Dean Everitt, feel there is some merit to these ideas, perhaps you can present them to our membership through the medium of the *Journal of Engineering Education*, and exhort future speakers at Annual Meetings to make that extra effort to speak their speeches—not read 'em!

Let our speakers be scholars who have toiled long hours in developing new solutions to problems in engineering education and who with zest and enthusiasm rush out into the marketplace, as did Archimedes, eager to proclaim to the world what they have found. Such men will share with their listeners—in words that will flow freely—the processes of thinking which nourished to maturity their newborn ideas.

These men—these teachers of men—will in this way impart far more to their colleagues and pupils than can be read from a printed page.

>William H. Crew
>Los Alamos Scientific Laboratory
>Los Alamos, New Mexico

July 3, 1956

Discussion and problems

1. List Dr. Crew's objections to papers which are read *word for word from copy?* In the particular situation described, do you think that his complaint is justified?
2. Do you think that Dr. Crew would have been satisfied with skillful speakers reading from a manuscript especially prepared for listeners? Explain.
3. What does the author mean when he says that speakers "impart far more to their colleagues and pupils than can be read from a printed page"? Do you agree?
4. Which of the following phrases do you think summarize Dr. Crew's complaint against reading *word for word from copy* at the annual meeting of the American Society of Engineering Education? inappropriate for the occasion or situation? inappropriate for the subject? inappropriate for the audience? inappropriate for the speaker?

So you're going to "read" a paper! *

Harold Haskitt, *Professor in the Department of Humanities at General Motors Institute, is currently conducting speech programs for middle and upper management groups at General Motors. His paper was originally prepared at the request and with the suport of the English Division, American Society of Engineering Education, as part of "Improve-the-Sessions" movement. It was probably aimed at improving the situation described by William H. Crew in the previous article, "Candid Comments on 'Reading' Papers." Haskitt reminds speakers that communication involves more than the transmission of thoughts.*

COMMUNICATION

With your permission I'm going to assume that you have been asked to "present" or "read" a "paper" at a convention session of your primary technical society. Your topic has been selected and the session chairman has indicated a definite time limit.—Now what do you do? If you are like most of us, you will proably get your notes together, *write* your "paper," have it mimeographed, run through it aloud a time or two, and then present it at the meeting by reading it in a not-too-effective way to your disappointed peers.

When you have finished, you breathe a sigh of relief and comfort yourself with the thought that you have made copies

---

* From Harold O. Haskitt, Jr., "So You're Going to 'Read' a Paper!" *Journal of Engineering Education* (January 1957), pp. 393-396. Reprinted by permission of ASEE and the author.

of the "paper" available in printed form—just in case someone didn't understand or remember what you had to say. If this has not happened to you personally, you perhaps can recall similar instances in convention situations where you have been the "listener" to such a talk. After such sessions you may have had the feeling, either as speaker or listener, that somehow it might have been better.

Somehow you were not satisfied that a good job of communicating had been done. But before you could get around to doing much thinking about how it might have been improved, you became involved in other activities and responsibilities which crowded it out of your mind until the next convention or the next speech. Toward the purpose of seeing what the speaker might do before his next talk, let's take a look at some of the elements in the complex process of getting ideas across to individuals in an audience.

Communication, not presentation, of ideas involves more than the transmission of thoughts by you as a speaker to or at a listener. At almost the same instant that the listener is receiving the thought-content of the talk, he is also receiving clues which he uses to build an evaluation of you as a person: professional expert, colleague, and fellow *human* being.

These things directly affect his feelings and attitudes as a listener, and may well determine how much of the thought (content) he understands and carries away with him. When an audience member goes away from a convention meeting saying, "I came to hear the *man*, not just his paper. I could have stayed at home and got more out of it by reading the speech myself," isn't he saying to a speaker, "I want to know both *you and* your ideas—please talk *with* me on a person-to-person basis, not *at* me as if I were a cabbagehead"?

The fact that in listening, a person *feels* at the same time that he *thinks*, accounts for the fast-growing use over the past few years of the extemporaneous method of speech delivery. Each listener wants to feel that the speaker is carrying on a friendly, high spirited, organized conversation with him (and the others in the group) on a subject which is highly informative and interesting to both parties in the discussion. Now, what can a convention speaker do to improve his chances of communicating effectively? The following may suggest ideas to you which you may find at least worth thinking about if not worth actually using at some time.

KNOW YOUR SUBJECT

It is almost too obvious that a good communicator must be saturated with his subject. The concepts you are going to discuss should be so thoroughly thought through that you will have no difficulty in capturing and recapturing the bases for each main point and its supporting details at the time you are bringing them out. Each idea expressed should stem from a clear-cut basis in thought, and, whenever possible, your visualization of ideas expressed should be vivid and intense.

Even the words you use should be carefully selected in terms of the pictures, concepts, and interest that they arouse, both in the speaker *and* the listener. For, generally speaking, the more a speaker knows and the sharper his perceptions are about a subject, the more interested he becomes in it, until he actually finds himself anxious to share it with others.

ORGANIZE FOR YOUR LISTENER

Body of the talk. The main reason for organizing material is to help the listener understand it more completely, more rapidly, and more easily, even with a minimum of effort.

This means then that the subject matter should be put together in a structural pattern which the listener can recall easily later on, and which he can recreate quickly for himself as the speaker is talking.

Main points should be limited in number (no more than five), and worded in a concise, clear, and interesting way. Explanations, illustrations, facts, and other supporting materials for these principal ideas should be selected to capture the greatest listener interest and understanding in the limited time allowed the speaker. If certain materials will cause audience interest to lag, they should be simplified, eliminated, or presented in a different way.

Introduction of the talk. The function of the introductory portion of a speech is to get the audience warmed up and in a receptive frame of mind to understand and accept the main ideas to be brought out. During this period a listener is very busy trying to focus his attention and to evaluate the elements that go to make up your particular personality. At the same time, he is trying to establish in his mind the specific central idea and your approach to it so that he can build his own "speech" as the talk unfolds.

So, sufficient time should be spent in developing whatever is used to arouse interest and lead into the main subject so that the audience can establish a favorable and receptive listening attitude. In addition to stating the central theme, some indication as to how you intend to develop the subject may help the listener in recognizing relationships between ideas as the speaker progresses.

Conclusion of the talk. Develop the conclusion so that the central and main ideas are clearly reinforced. Audience-interest should be maintained at a high level right up to the last syllable.

WRITE AND RE-WRITE

A paper that is to be published as an article after it is delivered as a speech will involve re-writing at least twice, and perhaps more—first as an article, then as a speech. Re-writing during the preparation of the article allows you to weigh and select words carefully, to cast them into phrases and sentences which will carry the precise meaning you want to convey to your *reader*. If you try to use the written paper as a manuscript from which to speak, however, you may have some difficulty.

Normally, the way we write and the way we speak differ considerably, primarily because of the contrast between a reader's situation and that of a listener at the time each is receiving the information. If a silent reader doesn't understand what is written the first time he reads it, he usually has time to go back and re-read a given sentence, paragraph, or even page before he goes on to the next unit. A listener, by contrast, has no "second chance," so-to-speak. He must get the speaker's meaning immediately because he usually cannot or does not ask the speaker to stop and repeat so that the puzzling sentence or unit can be "re-heard."

This obviously means that a speaker's language must be as simple and concrete as possible, his sentences relatively short, and his organizational pattern easy-to-follow if he is to communicate successfully. If you are going to read your paper aloud, consider re-writing it in the language and style you personally use in speaking, so that you will be direct and conversational in your approach to the audience. Incidentally, you may be surprised how much easier it is not only on you but also on your listeners.

SHARPEN YOUR SPEECH DELIVERY

In the actual delivery of the speech there are obviously two major methods available to you, both of which are equally effective if done well. One, already mentioned, is to use the written paper in developing a speech manuscript suitable for easy, conversational, oral reading. The other is to speak from a brief outline or notes.

During the preparation stage of either of these two methods, one way to assure coverage of all the main ideas and supports, and at the same time to find the best way for you to express these ideas aloud, is to develop a good old-fashioned outline in standard form, including Introduction, Body, and Conclusion. If you use the first method of delivery (speaking from a manuscript), it will help you to find and decide upon certain word choices and ways of putting sentences together which will allow you to be conversational and direct with your audience. The resulting style will make it much easier for you to *feel* and *think* the ideas *as you are reading the words.*

Once you have settled upon the exact wording and sentence structure for the completed speech manuscript, it should be rehearsed aloud word for word, with as much meaning and real feeling behind the ideas as you can get it. Continue revisions until you are satisfied that the manuscript will allow you to be yourself.

A tape recorder can be an excellent aid to you, not only in the process of developing the final speech manuscript, but also in improving the way you read it aloud. If you record your practice readings and listen carefully to the playbacks, you will hear many things which will encourage you. You may also hear a few things you might like to change, such as putting more emphasis upon certain important ideas, developing more speaker-interest in parts or even throughout the talk, or sharpening your person-to-person manner of talking while you read—to mention only a few.

If you find it easier to maintain audience interest by speaking from a brief outline or notes, the use of a tape recorder during practice sessions will give you additional help in spotting areas where you may wish to strengthen your own concepts, or perhaps make even better use of your voice in getting the intended meaning across. A few such recording and playback practice sessions can be very rewarding.

"SEE" EACH LISTENER

During the actual delivery of the talk at the meeting, a speaker needs his own continuous index of "feedback." That is, he *must establish and maintain* definite *eye contact* with as many individuals as he possibly can during the speech, so that each person will feel that *he* individually is being included in the speaker's audience. By this means you can evaluate your own progress and success in getting your thoughts and feelings across and can adjust accordingly as you move along. When visual aids are used, you should be so familiar with their nature and content that good eye contact with the group can be maintained even while working with the aid.

One last word about the speaker's *enthusiasm* both before, and on the day of the talk. You not only should check your visual aids and other materials before the meeting time, but you should also prepare yourself psychologically. Your feelings of friendliness and enthusiasm about your subject matter and the opportunity to share it with your peers in this particular group of associates and other professional people must be so vital and intense that they will be infectious to everyone, even those in the back row. Let the group share with you the proper pride you have in your subject, your chosen profession, and in your status as a fellow human being.

A little spontaneous feeling can send a thought a long way.

Discussion and problems

1. What is the author's definition or feeling about *communication?* How does this definition help to account for the popularity of extemporaneous delivery?
2. Haskitt advises the speaker to know his subject. What must a speaker know about his subject?
3. What must the speaker remember about the body, introduction, and conclusion of a talk?
4. What differences are noted between a manuscript for publication and one for reading?
5. What doesn't Haskitt insist on in one form of delivery—either a manuscript to be read, or extemporaneous delivery from notes or an outline? Do you think that a speaker reading a manuscript allows the kind of communication desired by Haskitt?
6. What are the advantages of developing an outline when preparing a speech?
7. How can a tape recorder help in preparing and practicing a speech? Can you think of any limitations of practicing with only a tape recorder?
8. How can eye contact be practiced? What are its advantages?
9. Do you think that enthusiasm in a speaker is a necessary requirement for communication with an audience? Can enthusiasm be "practiced"? What do you think that Haskitt

means when he says that a speaker should prepare himself "psychologically"?

10 Practice a ten-fifteen minute technical speech (extemporaneously, or reading a manuscript prepared for listeners) with a tape recorder, and then in the presence of one or two friends. To what extent are both forms of practice helpful? Play the tape recording for a class or group of friends. What is their reaction compared with your usual "live" presentation?

How to organize the oral version of a technical paper *

***William J. Temple**, Professor Emeritus of Speech at Brooklyn College, and a Fellow of the American Association for the Advancement of Science, is an advocate of carefully selecting and organizing material for the oral version of a technical paper. Realizing that listening and speaking present two different situations, Dr. Temple offers concrete advice on how to prepare a paper for listeners. Selectivity of information and simplicity of structure are important principles for every technical speaker.*

LISTENER VS. READER

Recent papers and editorials in the *Proceedings of the IRE* [1,2] have strongly advised that, in presenting technical material before professional groups, an author should never merely read aloud the paper he has prepared for publication in print. It is the purpose of this article to make a few practical suggestions for the preparation of an oral version of

---

* From William J. Temple, "Preparing the Oral Version of a Technical Paper," *Proceedings of the IRE* (March 1948), pp. 388-389. Reprinted by permission of IEEE and the author.
[1] W. L. Everitt, "The Presentation of Technical Developments before Professional Societies," *Proc. IRE*, Vol. 33, pp. 423-425 (July 1945).
[2] Arthur C. Downes, "Proper Presentation of Papers before Technical Meetings," *Proc. IRE*, Vol. 35, p. 235 (March 1947).

such a paper. Most of these suggestions are derived from standard textbooks.[3,4]

If you will recall your own experiences as a listener in a meeting and as a reader at your own desk you will see that there are very good reasons for you as an author, to adopt two different methods of composing your material to suit these two different situations.

At your own desk, with a printed article before you, you can peruse it at your own pace and take as much time as you need to absorb it. You can read and re-read a crucial paragraph. You can take the time to puzzle out the meaning of a difficult or complicated sentence. If the writer uses an unfamiliar word, you can look it up. If you are interrupted, or if your attention wanders, or if you go to sleep, you can resume your reading later, going back to the beginning of the article, if need be, to pick up the thread of development. As a listener, you can do none of these things.

These reflections indicate that the oral version of a paper should differ from its printed version in two important ways. Designed for aural rather than visual reception, it should be shorter, and it should be simpler in structure. And, if you are going to avoid the soporific monotony with which almost everyone except a professional actor or a radio announcer reads aloud, you must prepare to present your material by *talking*, not reading aloud or reciting from memory. Speaking is more natural, more vivid, and more direct than writing or reading, and these advantages are worth more than the additional effort required for thorough preparation. The suggestions which follow are intended to give you practical hints

---

[3] J. M. O'Neill (editor), *Foundations of Speech*, Prentice-Hall, Inc., New York, N.Y., 1941.
[4] Alan H. Monroe, *Principles of Speech* (Brief Edition), Scott, Foresman and Company, Chicago, Ill., 1945.

on abbreviating and simplifying your material, and preparing an oral presentation of it.

SELECTIVITY

In the first place, you must beware of the temptation to include everything you have to say in your oral version. Speaking is much slower than silent reading. In print, an author can sometimes afford to express himself exhaustively. In an oral presentation, neither the time limit nor the listeners' patience will permit anything but a selective treatment. Furthermore, an article, even in a technical journal, reaches a larger and presumably more general audience. In delivering a talk, the speaker must address himself to the group of individual listeners immediately confronting him, and he may touch lightly on matters which he would spell out carefully in writing even for technically informed readers.

In remembering the necessity for keeping within a time limit, you must remember also that the listener's capacity for absorbing detail is not so great as the reader's. The desire for full and complete treatment in a limited time may lead you into the mistake of using a compressed, compact style which is suitable only for reading and study with concentration. If you include too much detail for the sake of accuracy, you may find that you have sacrificed clarity. A graph shows more at a glance than the table of data from which it was constructed. A block diagram is more legible than a photograph of the apparatus.

SIMPLICITY OF STRUCTURE

The second suggestion is simplicity of structure. Clarity is largely the result of simplicity. The listener will go away from the meeting remembering what you have said if you have analyzed your material thoroughly and presented it in two or three or four (the fewer the better) clearly labeled main parts. If you can arrange your main points in a way that makes sense, label them plainly, and notify your listeners when you leave one and begin another, you make it easy for them to follow you. You also make it easier for them to remember what you have said, because you have provided pegs on which to hang the details.

Arrange your details under your main headings in orderly sequence. Common types of sequence are those of time, space, cause and effect, and special topical arrangements. Your main topics should follow one kind of sequence, but there is no rule against using different types under different main headings. Perhaps it should be unnecessary to add that you should not jump back and forth from one main topic to another in presenting your material. The more thorough and logical your analysis and arrangement, the less likely you are to skip around in delivering your talk.

INTRODUCTIONS AND CONCLUSIONS

Having set the limits of your talk and selected your main divisions and arranged your material tentatively in your mind or on paper, you are ready to consider your introduction and conclusion, and to begin to think about the actual words you plan to use in talking to your audience.

The function of an introduction is to get the attention of your listeners and to give them some reason for continuing to listen to you. If your name and your subject have appeared in the printed program of the meeting, a part of this function has been performed for you, and you may assume that at least some of the people present are there because they want to hear what you have to say. Nevertheless, it is important in preparing your talk for you to ask yourself this question: "Why should *these* people listen to *me* discuss *this* subject at *this* time?" Write out the answer to this question. It will focus your attention on the four important factors in every public-speaking situation: the audience, the speaker, the subject, and the occasion. If there is a good reason for your audience to listen to you, it will be found in one or more of these factors. Plan in your introductory remarks to tell them why they need to know what you have to say, and support your statement as you would any main point, illustrating the need by an incident or example, reinforcing your statement by additional examples or facts, and pointing out the direct relation of the subject to their professional interests. This part of your speech should be short (probably a tenth or less of its length), but it is important. Do not omit it.

The function of the conclusion is to summarize or recapitulate the main ideas of your talk, to draw attention to important conclusions, and to reinforce by restatement or application whatever important impression you wish to leave in your listeners' minds.

A generalized skeleton outline of a report based on this plan might look something like the following:

A MODEL OUTLINE

Introduction
   I. (After addressing the chair and the audience). Opening statement designed to get attention (reference to your subject or the immediate circumstances of your talk; rhetorical question; startling statement or quotation; humorous story, *if apt*)

    A. Support for statement
        1. Detail
        2. Detail
    B. Further Support
        1, 2, etc. (details)
II. Restatement
III. Statement telling why your listeners need your information
    A. Support (illustration)
        1, 2, etc. (details)
    B. Further support (additional facts or example)
IV. Statement relating subject directly to present audience
    A, B, etc. (supporting statements)
V. Summary statement or restatement
VI. Preliminary summary of subject (enumeration of main parts or other clear indication of direction in which you intend to lead your listeners)

Body
    I. Statement of first main part of subject
        A. Support
            1. Detail
            2, 3, etc. (details)
        B, C, etc. Further development of first main part
    II, III, etc. Second third, etc., main parts

Conclusion
    I. Final Summary
        A. Recapitulation of main points
        B. Important conclusions
        C. Reinforcement (perhaps by referring again to listeners' need for your information)

WORDING

When you have fitted your material to such an outline you may feel that the principal part of your work is finished, but there are two further steps in preparation which will add greatly to your own comfort and confidence on the platform, and, incidentally, to the comfort and edification of your listeners. The first of these is to clothe your outline with words, and the second is to practice delivering your talk aloud.

In choosing the actual words you will use in delivering your talk, you may have to experiment to find the method that is best suited to you. Some speakers prefer to write out a full draft so that they will not have to depend on the inspiration of the moment for striking, accurate, or thoughtful phraseology. Others, realizing that very few people can write as spontaneously and vigorously as they talk, combine the last two steps in preparation by taking the detailed outline to a private place where they can go through the material aloud, as if talking to a friend.

Whether you write it out first or not, practice aloud is the best way to fix the sequence of your ideas in your mind and to try out variations of wording. It is at this stage that you should time yourself and revise your plan accordingly.

REHEARSAL

The final stage of preparation for delivery is to put your outline or manuscript in your pocket and go through your talk without looking at the paper. Rehearse it, as you will deliver it, on your feet. If you have access to a recording device, use it; any office dictating machine will serve the purpose. In listening to the record you may learn something profitable about your vocal powers and limitations and about your distinctness of utterance.

The best kind of final rehearsal is a tryout performance before a group as much as possible like your ultimate audience. If you can arrange to talk about your subject in a seminar or in a conference of your colleagues, you will get a great deal of value from the experience.

These suggestions may be carried out in various ways. You may decide to prepare first the version of your paper destined for print, abbreviating it and simplifying it for oral delivery. Or, you may start with the oral version and rewrite it for publication, as Everitt suggests, so as to take advantage of the criticism and discussion precipitated by your presentation. Whichever you do, remember that, as Downes points out, "The presentation of a well-prepared abbreviated version will not in any way detract from the value to those in the audience more familiar with the general subject of the paper, since they can study it in detail on publication, and will hold the interest of the entire audience." And that "the papers most vividly remembered are those presented as though the author were talking to a few friends." Don't read before them—talk to them.

Discussion and problems

1 What differences does Temple describe between a listening and a reading situation?
2 In what two specific ways should an oral version of a paper differ from a printed version? Why does Temple prefer *talking* to reading a paper or reciting from memory?
3 The author notes that common types of sequence in the body of a talk are "those of time, space, cause and effect, and special topical arrangements." Give examples of each of these patterns? Can you think of other patterns that might be used to develop the body of a technical talk?

4   What are the functions of introductions and conclusions, and what information needs to be included in each? Why does Temple stress the importance of the introduction?
5   What methods of rehearsal does Temple advocate?
6   Would you agree that although Temple advises an informal presentation (*talking* rather than reading), he strongly urges the formal selection and organization of material? Do you think that he overemphasizes the importance of outlining?
7   Temple offers a generalized skeleton outline of an oral report. Using this outline as a model, write out a specific, detailed, and concrete outline for a fifteen minute technical talk. What types of sequence are used to develop the body of your talk? How helpful is the outline in organizing your material? in delivering it?

The professional presentation of scientific papers *

Harold G. Cassidy, Professor in Chemistry at Yale University and a Fellow of the American Association for the Advancement of Science, has published numerous research papers, essays, and books. His advice on technical speaking reflects a concern for organizing, stating, and delivering ideas in a professional manner. Although Dr. Cassidy refers to his article as "a checklist of points to be considered," he frequently illustrates his rules.

CONVEYING INFORMATION

A well-prepared subject, elegantly expressed by a speaker who is convinced that he has something to say, can be a joy to listen to. It can be a joy to him who gives it, for he can see the light of intelligent comprehension in the faces of his audience, and he can sense that his presentation has the marks of craftsmanship upon it. Every one gains from such an exchange.

How does he do it? Can you, whether an undergraduate, a graduate student, or an instructor, learn how to get the most out of your own talents, and perhaps experience this pleasure yourself? From my own experience with students I can say that the answer is "Yes." Given the will to take

---

* From Harold G. Cassidy, "The Professional Presentation of Scientific Papers," *Journal of Chemical Education* (July 1963), pp. 373-376. Reprinted by permission of the publisher and author.

pains, to prepare, and to believe in himself, any intelligent person can become a good speaker. With imagination and ideas, he can become excellent.

In order to help those who would wish to examine and perhaps improve their presentation of scientific papers, I have drawn up a checklist of points to be considered. It has come from observing the reactions of audiences to lecturers, from listening to a considerable number of bad lectures and a small number of magnificent ones, and from reading books and articles on the subject. This checklist is offered here.

I assume throughout that you are not trying to incite the audience, or make a secial appeal, or give a hortatory talk, or even to entertain, but to convey information. Your effort, then, is at communication. Here three factors can be considered, for the sake of clarity, though all are interrelated: the talk itself, the part played by you, and matters affecting the audience more personally.

THE SPEECH

Prepare beforehand. My wife knew a preacher who boasted that he never prepared his sermons: all he had to do was stand in the pulpit, and the Lord put the words into his mouth. But it was remarked frequently by the congregation that the Lord must have been occupied elsewhere. So, even though you have been living with the work, have just turned off the last stopcock, and made the last calculation, for the work you are about to report, *write it out.* It is instructive how many questions of organization suddenly turn up, how many decisions about what to include, and how many questions that require going to the literature. One or two of these, suddenly rearing their ugly heads while you are on your feet, can demoralize a talk even though the speaker may survive. I do not feel put-upon if a 45- to 50-minute talk needs 30 to 50 hours preparation for writing, revising, documenting, and rewriting. A recent Sigma Xi lecture [1] was revised some eight times before and during its presentation on a tour, and the book on which it has been based was completely rewritten seven times over about ten years.[2]

Don't try to cover too much. Very few lectures can have the compactness that is permitted in a written communication. The English language is about 50% redundant,[3] a feature which helps to combat "noise" and aids in getting the message through. Even so, you need to repeat and use several images, perhaps, to get your point across over the "noises" of all kinds that beset you. These may be external to the auditorium or lecture rooms—whose location often seems close to a truck route; or internal—you can include faulty public address systems, audience inattention, and so on.

Use illustrations wherever possible. But again, don't try to cover too much. Make this simple calculation, and then shudder as the speaker brings in 60 slides for a 50-minute talk. If a scientific slide is well prepared and presented it can be used for a full minute or two. A slide per minute for fifty minutes becomes a travelog, but rarely a scientific talk. To show *all* the data is a great temptation to the novice who is perhaps justly proud of his tenacity and perspicuity in gathering it; but he should severely resist the temptation. The best cure is for him to attend one of the general sessions

---

[1] Cassidy, H. G., "The Problem of the Sciences and the Humanities, a Diagnosis and a Prescription," in *Science in Progress*, 12th series, Brode, W. R., ed., Yale University Press, New Haven, Conn. 1962, pp. 93-116.
[2] Cassidy, H. G. *The Sciences and the Arts, A New Alliance*, Harper & Brothers, New York, 1962.
[3] Shannon, C. E., and Weaver, W., *The Mathematical Theory of Communication*, University of Illinois Press, Urbana, 1959, p. 104.

at a national scientific meeting. One or two horrible examples can save more souls than much exhortation.

Be sure slides are clean. I well remember attending a lecture on the Islands of the Aegean. The effect was totally destroyed by a large thumbprint in the center of every sky. Be harsh with the projectionist if necessary—but usually he will be careful about holding the slides, and *you* will have to get them clean. The old rule is "Right thumb in the upper right-hand corner only, and then the slides will be properly set." Remember, too, that unsupported film can melt. If the slides are films, put them between glass plates.

Preferably don't read the paper. If necessary, memorize it. Or type it down one side of the page, leaving a two-inch margin on the left (or right). In this put a *few* key prompting words, written large. I also introduce a red asterisk for each slide—and any necessary data about the slide in case detailed questions are asked. In any event, be sure the slides are in order. The speaker surprised by his own slide-arrangement does not convey confidence in the rest of his talk.

Sometimes I read passages when I want to be very precise; but I keep remembering a story told by Yale Professor Samuel Hemingway of the famous visiting lecturer who sat before a packed house in Strathcona Auditorium and read from the galley proofs of his forthcoming book—pausing to make corrections and cross out errors! He was never invited back.

Start simply; if possible speak simply. Tell what you are going to do, without giving away the climax. Use a range of emphasis and inflection; keep the sentences short unless you have an infallible sense for dependent clauses. This is a rare gift. Avoid dangling constructions and sentences that go nowhere. Technical jargon that might be necessary in a written work should be avoided if possible in a spoken address.

Especially eschew long variants of recognized words: irregardless, confliction, analyzation, commercialistic, optimization, (and suboptimization) and (shudder!) tangibilitate. What may happen with jargon is that a lecture sounds as though it *might* make sense. We have all had this experience, and I recall an item that appeared in the Arthur D. Little bulletin some years ago [4] called "The Turbo-Encabulator." I quote only the first and last paragraphs to give some flavor of it.

For a number of years now work has been proceeding in order to bring perfection to the crudely conceived idea of a machine that would not only supply inverse reactive current for use in unilateral phase detractors, but would also be capable of automatically synchronizing cardinal grammeters. Such a machine is the 'Turbo-Encabulator.' Basically, the only new principle involved is that instead of power being generated by the relaxive motion of conductors and fluxes, it is produced by the modial interaction of magnetoreluctance and capacitive directance. . . .

Undoubtedly, the turbo-encabulator has now reached a very high level of technical development. It has been successfully used for operating nofer trunnions. In addition wherever a barescent skar motion is required, it may be employed in conjunction with a deep-drawn reciprocating dingle arm to reduce sinussoidal depleneration.

If these passages are read to an audience in a firm and well-modulted voice, with emphasis on the more unlikely words, many people are impressed even though vaguely disturbed.

---

[4] The full text of this significant contribution to scientific thought may be obtained from the public relations department of Arthur D. Little, Inc., Acorn Park, Cambridge, Mass., 02140. It is entitled "The Turbo-Encabulator in Industry," and its author is Mr. J. H. Quick, of the Institution of Electrical Engineers, London, England. It was published in that institution's *Students' Quarterly Journal*, December 1944.

Repeat major points and introduce one or two interim summaries. This can help the audience, and at the same time it can be used to develop a climax.

Try to work towards some climax. This should preferably be one in which the preceding data all fall into place, or in which much falls into place, but some open questions are left. It is the height of artistry to let the audience—or some members of it—get the point themselves just before you state it.

Give full credit. The audience knows you didn't do all that work. If you actually did, you may even have to drop a gentle hint that you really did.

THE SPEAKER

Posture is important. Try to be poised, calm, confident (but not overconfident). If you are nervous, there are tricks you can use to steady yourself. You can *slowly* adjust the cuff of your right sleeve with your left hand; you can remove your glasses slowly, to make a point. Watch how others do it. But don't lean on the desk or blackboard; don't fidget, or wriggle. I well remember my first public talk; it was to the entire population of Central High School, in Akron, Ohio. I had to present an award to one of the seniors for winning an essay contest put on by an honor fraternity in the university. I was so scared I could not keep my knees steady, and soon the entire front row of seniors were knocking their knees in unison! It was a traumatic experience for me.

Keep your hands out of your pockets, especially if they have chalk dust on them: few speakers can bring off the image of the untidy thinker unaware of the chalk dust smudges all over his dark suit.

Use the blackboard intelligently. Write on it clearly—print if you can—and large enough to be seen at the back of the room (test it if you are not sure). Let your formulas and structural diagrams be crisp and well drawn, not hurried and sloppy. Write with elegance. Don't stand in front of what you have written unless there is some reason for it to be kept from the audience, and *please* don't erase immediately, or suddenly change signs throughout. Give your compulsive and other note-takers a break. Also, *please*, erase completely and smoothly. Shards of previous writing left on the board by the erratic or swirler types of erasure-pattern makers can become confusing subscripts or exponents or even peculiar functional groups on later writing.

Remember that the pointer can be a weapon. There are two types of these weapons: rods and optical beam pointers. Rods should be used almost touching the screen so that the point of the shadow and that of the rod coincide. Few things are more annoying than to use the *shadow* of the pointer as an indicator, without letting the audience in on this off-beat trick. Don't touch the beaded screen with the pointer. A well-practiced screen-scraper can gouge a rain of beads from the screen with wild gyrations, and make the owner of the screen quite nervous. Use the pointer to point, not waggle; and when through with it, lay it down.

The light-spot or arrow pointer is a more dangerous weapon. Examine it beforehand, and learn how to focus it and to turn it off. Hardly anything is more fascinatedly demoralizing than the jiggling, winking, blinding spot, waved at the audience; or the woven arabesques on the ceiling and walls of the room made by the careless lecturer who has failed to turn the light off and put it down; or the fuzzy spot of the unfocused beam pointing doubtfully at some region of a slide. If your hand is not steady, use both hands, or steady them with elbow on the lectern or desk-top.

Avoid monotonous gestures. Sawing with the arm, stiff motions, stalking prey behind the lectern, and so on, are to be avoided.

Talk slowly enough to be understood, with a well-modulated and controlled voice. Pause occasionally where emphasis is needed and, when a beginner, get some honest friend to listen to you and tell you about speech idiosyncrasies. I once timed a very nervous graduate student in an average of twenty "uh's," "er's," and "ah's" per minute over a five-minute period; this is very hard on the audience.

Be very careful of expressions that can be misinterpreted or twisted by the sophomoric minds present in every audience. Most of these that we have experienced cannot be printed, but a misplaced titter can be devastating. Remember that there are many ways of saying things. One man says "When I saw you, Time stood still." Another might say, "Your face would stop a clock."

It is very helpful to have demonstration material wherever possible (big enough to be seen). This is made most effective if it is hidden from view—behind the desk, or in a paper bag—until just the right moment when it can be brought out to contribute to one of the high points or to a climax in the talk.

Plan ahead. If much material is to be put on the blackboard, make up a drawing of the board with items arranged on it. If possible try it out ahead of time, and plan so that you can leave material as long as possible on the board as you work across it. This can be used for reference, and is very greatly appreciated by the audience. As you proceed by planned stages, writing everything out, or drawing diagrams, the whole talk takes on structure and increased intelligibility. Blackboard technique is an art.

THE AUDIENCE

Avoid apologies. "I really don't know too much about this"; I really haven't prepared"; "I just tossed together a few notes at the last minute." The audience may believe you and some may leave (mentally). In any case if true it will become all too apparent and doesn't need explicit statement; and it doesn't put you or the audience at ease.

No snide remarks. Along with avoiding apologies which belittle yourself, avoid belittling others. It is *not* funny to make puns on names. If you prove someone's work to be in error, be charitable. Perhaps he did not know as much as you now know. Science is cumulative. The speaker who wonders out loud in public how some scientist of fifty years ago missed some observation (while *he*, of course, saw it, with brilliant results) nauseates the more perceptive members of the audience and may convict himself as a fool if, as is often the case, there did not exist means for such observation at that time. Remember that high-vacuum and molecular distillation, UV, IR, NMR, glass electrodes, vacuum tube voltmeters and recorders, chromatography of all kinds, and most of the accessory instrumentation were just not available—or even not invented—fifty years ago or, some of them, ten or fifteen years ago. In any case, intellectual arrogance is one of the real sins that a speaker, or scholar, can commit. Be *ye* not guilty of it.

Never show disappointment. What if the equipment is poor, or nonexistent? Make do, with calm acceptance. After all, the chairman and the program committee may be embarrassed, too. *Never* worry about the size of the audience.

Remember that the audience didn't have to come, and they don't have to listen.

Don't make the audience feel insecure. Excessive erudition of the gratuitous kind is to be avoided. But the audience loves it if you lead them into a nice point that they see before you state it.

Don't make the audience angry. There are many ways to be insulting. Dress to show that the occasion is important. One of the worst results of the beatnik approach is that the speaker implies to the audience that he lacks self-respect. Perceptive members of the audience react accordingly. You can be informal without being sloppy.

Local custom should be attended to. I recall one Summer Science Seminar in Bozeman, Montana, when it was very hot. I had to give a series of lectures. The first day I turned up with seersucker suit and tie. No-one had on a jacket. The next day I appeared without jacket. No-one had on a tie. The next day I was handed a gift-wrapped package, courtesy of the Director of the Program, with the request that I open and act accordingly. I left the room and returned, as instructed, wearing the loudest Truman-type yellow, green, and black sport shirt imaginable. I read aloud the gift card to the group: "To introduce you to the Montana Ivy League Look."

Start on time. A common insult to the audience is the late start; start on time. This may require that you annoy the program chairman somewhat.

Sum up briefly. But tell the audience what you have told them—in the large.

SIMPLICITY, SIMPLICITY

I hope that this checklist will be helpful to undergraduates, graduate students, and all those who wish to or have to speak about scientific subjects. I am sure that it is not exhaustive—human beings are full of ingenuity. But at least it can be used as a basis upon which you can construct your own list. So I conclude, in summary, with an anonymous quotation that appeared in a newspaper at least twenty years ago. I cannot give the author credit because I don't know who he is.

In promulgating your esoteric cogitations or in articulating superficial sentimentalities, philosophical profundities or psychological prognoses, beware of platitudinous ponderosity. Eschew jejune babblement and asinine affection. Let even your extemporaneous discantations and unpremeditated expatiations have vivacity and intelligibility without rodomontade or thrasonical bombast. Sedulously suppress any polysyllabic propensities, paraphrastic euphuism, psittocaceous vacuities, ventriloquial verbosity and multiloquial bravardage. Shun double-entendre, prurient jocosity, and pestiferous, ingustible, or turgid profanity, whether obscure or apparent. In short, speak clearly, plainly, simply.

Discussion and problems

1 In stressing the importance of preparation, why does Cassidy advise the speaker to write out and revise his talk although he may be an expert on the subject? Might a detailed outline accomplish the same purpose?
2 What information needs to be repeated in a technical talk? Why?
3 Why does Cassidy advise a speaker against showing *all* of his data? What alternative would you suggest?
4 Why should a technical speaker avoid using dangling constructions, technical jargon, and the "long variants of recognized words"? Give your own examples of these shortcomings.
5 Give examples of organizational techniques that "work toward some climax."

6 How should a speaker plan the use of material to put on a blackboard? What other advice does the author give for using a blackboard?
7 What effect do apologies and snide remarks have on an audience? Give some examples from your own experience as a listener. List other ways a speaker might unintentionally anger or irritate an audience.
8 Summarize Cassidy's advice to a technical speaker? What does he mean by "professional presentation" of scientific information?

Some notes on oral communication at scientific meetings *

A. L. Bacharach, *a Fellow of the Royal Institute of Chemistry, is the author and editor of numerous books and papers on drugs, nutrition, and biochemistry. Drawing on half a century of experience in the communication of scientific facts, the author lays down a number of principles for scientists who wish to become successful speakers. Statements such as "don't flap your hands at the screen or waggle fingers at figures on it" humorously and forcefully remind the reader that the oral presentation of scientific information is an art often neglected.*

PRINCIPLES OF ORAL COMMUNICATION

(1) *Time.* Stick closely to the allotted period. If you have any doubt about how long you are going to take, and wish to avoid being cut off by the chairman in the flower of your argument, have a rehearsal and adopt whatever steps are necessary to ensure that you have a margin of 5–10% of the time allotted. Only in this way can you make possible a reasonable discussion of your communication, as well as gaining a distinctly increased measure of popularity among the audience (should this be possible). Anyone but an experienced speaker would be foolish to present a paper orally without a rehearsal anyway.

---

* From A. L. Bacharach, "Some Notes on Oral Communication at Scientific Meetings," *Chemistry and Industry*, published by the Society of Chemical Industry, London (October 3, 1959), pp. 1244-1245. Reprinted by permission of the author.

(2) *Hearing.* Ask your best friend to tell you whether you have got the kind of voice that has the remotest chance of being heard at the back of the average hall or lecture theatre. Two out of five speakers—at any rate on their first appearances—have not. If you can't be heard by at least 80% of those present—and those who don't hear you are almost bound by the cussedness of nature to be just those whose opinion you most value—you will do damage to the reputation of your subject, your institution, your department, your chief, and yourself. If you can't be heard, you would much better not be there. Further, those who can't hear you will be debarred from taking any useful part in the discussion of your communication, which in my view is the main, if not the only, justification for your making it.

(3) *Extempore talking.* Do not read your manuscript, whether this be the complete "paper" prepared for publication or a specially composed summary or the pre-abstract as printed on the agenda paper. If you cannot talk for 20, 25 or 30 minutes from notes on a subject about which you are so expert that you have been invited to do so, or for 8 to 10 minutes on a piece of work that you, or you and your colleagues, have recently completed, surely "someone has erred." If the worst comes to the worst, and you fear that you can't survive eight minutes more or less extempore talking from a few notes, for heaven's sake prepare a written summary for the occasion and learn it by heart. If you did "repetition" at school, you surely have not entirely lost the faculty.

(4) *Slides.* See that your slides, if any, conform to the general principles already laid down by several societies and published by them. Don't have more than three slides per five minutes of "speaking time" unless you want to fail in both showing them all and saying about them what you

want in the time allotted. Your slides must be intelligible even to those in the audience who by chance cannot hear what you are saying about them (e.g., both abscissae and ordinates should be properly marked to show what they represent and in what units), and it follows that, above all things, they must be legible (even at the back of the hall or theatre) and not overcrowded. Use really black ink for matter to be photographed, and don't rely on a junior lab. boy to produce negatives of adequate contrast without your supervision. Refrain from just photographing published tables from your own or someone else's published papers. They are seldom sufficiently clear when so reproduced on the screen, they almost always contain more material than can be taken in and evaluated during a short showing as slides, and to use them is a piece of gratuitous rudeness to your audience: It implies that you don't think they can read the literature of the subject as well as you can, and it tells them that you really couldn't be bothered to prepare a simplified slide, showing the guts of the matter, just for the likes of them on so unimportant an occasion. If that's your view, you shouldn't be there anyhow.

(5) *Facing the audience.* Remember that you are not transparent or even translucent. When you are showing a slide, talk to the audience and not, as five speakers out of six still do, to the image on the screen. You will almost certainly be inaudible to some in the audience if you do that and will certainly not be as audible to any one there as if you faced him. If your slide needs explanation (which it shouldn't) or comment (which it may), you must ensure that this is heard. Assuming that the details on your slide are not so familiar to you that you can talk about them without looking at them—and they ought to be—adopt a simple de-

vice when you are having the slide made. Have a print made at the same time (it will cost you 6d. or less) and have this in front of you while the slide is being shown. Then you will be able to expound with minimum use of the pointer that is provided on the platform at all scientific meetings. Incidentally, if you must point, use that pointer and don't flap your hands at the screen or waggle fingers at figures on it.

(6) *Omitting niceties.* Time is precious, and it is therefore permissible to omit formalities—suitable at political meetings, public dinners, inaugural lectures, and similar solemn occasions, but entirely unnecessary at scientific meetings, especially when a long list of communications is to be made. You might omit:

(a) the words "Mr. chairman, ladies and gentlemen" any or all of them;
(b) more than a couple of sentences by way of historical introduction;
(c) bibliographical references to former work (your own or others), except just names of authors (and initials when needed for discrimination);
(d) acknowledgments to colleagues, assistants, employers, benefactors.

Items under (b), (c), and (d) will necessarily all be included in your complete paper as submitted for publication, and your past and present collaborators—of one kind and another—will there be duly credited with their contributions to the subject. If, however, the results of your work are unfortunately never published, those collaborators are not likely to complain about the non-acknowledgment of the part they played in your little tragedy.

LECTURING

These notes, drawn up more in sorrow than in anger and based upon about fifty years' somewhat embittering experience, were written with the "oral communication" of original work primarily in mind. I believe, all the same, that they apply largely also to the delivery of the more or less formal "lecture." Here, moreover, since you will be present as a result of direct invitation, presumably because you are assumed to know and to be able to communicate your subject, you have as great, if not a greater, responsibility both to your audience and to your own reputation as if you were only reporting the results of your own researches.

The main difference in technique will be determined by the fact that the "lecture" is almost always timed to last an hour, or even longer. That means for most lecturers a more or less complete script. With this before you the temptation discussed under (3) above will prove well-nigh irresistible, but resist it you must. Even if you do find it necessary to read exactly what you have written, you must as far as possible appear not to.

There are two primary reasons for this. First, "being read aloud to" is recognised as one of the most potent forms of hypnosis known; it is the rarest possible thing for anyone but a professional actor to be able to keep an audience awake while he is reading aloud to it. Secondly, it is extremely difficult, if not impossible, to be heard at the back of most halls and lecture theatres, and even at the front of some, if you have to keep your head bent down over the typescript in front of you.

For these reasons I entreat you when you have to deliver a "lecture" to do, if it is at all possible, exactly what I am recommending to those making scientific communications, that is, to dispense with a script altogether and speak from notes only—or even simply from the sequence of slides, best by making use of the technique outlined at the end of (4) above.

There is a further reason for not reading a typewritten script. You are almost certain to be asked nine times out of ten to supply the text of your lecture for publication. The forms of a lecture best suited for oral and written delivery are not the same. If you have a script carefully prepared for the former purpose, you will almost certainly be asked (anyhow you ought to be) to recast it for printing. If, however, you have prepared a form suitable as "the written word," you will save some wretched editor a lot of work and time and you should, moreover, be able to use this script as a guide to some more or less extempore oral delivery of your subject matter. But see also (3) above about the temptation to use as slides photographs of complex tabular matter that can be entirely suited to the more leisurely scrutiny it may deserve and even get when your lecture is published.

If it is possible to summarise in a single sentence what I have written above, perhaps it might be "It's no good at all knowing what you want to say unless you also know how to say it."

Discussion and problems

1 In your own words summarize Bacharach's principles of orally communicating scientific information. Give examples illustrating his principles.
2 What does the author believe to be the main justification for the oral communication of scientific information and how is it related to one of his guidelines?
3 Why does Bacharach feel that a lecturer has a greater responsibility to an audience than a scientist reporting his own research?

4 Why does Bacharach believe that scientists should speak extemporaneously and not read from a prepared manuscript?
5 Explain how a speaker might speak from a sequence of simplified slides that "show the guts of the matter." Can you think of any possible dangers in this technique?
6 What is the tone of the article? Do you think that Bacharach's use of wit and humor helps in developing his principles? Point out some examples.

How to master the art of reading speeches *

James F. Bender, author of several books on speech communication, heads his own firm of business consultants. In the following article, Dr. Bender does not discuss extensively the differences of a manuscript prepared for listeners vs. readers. He assumes, however, that oral reading can successfully communicate ideas if the speaker carefully practices his delivery. Twelve suggestions are listed so that a manuscript reader can gain the understanding and attention of his audience.

GOALS OF READING A SPEECH

Have you noticed how often sales executives read to their audiences at a convention or sales meeting? When they read well, they make a real contribution to the success of the program. When they read ineptly, they make a poor impression; the audience is bored; the program sags.

As an executive, you owe it to yourself to master the skill of reading aloud well—whether a speech before a convention, minutes to a committee, or a report to a sales meeting.

The late F.D.R. was a superb oral reader—not a great or even a good extempore speaker. He read his manuscripts as if he were chatting with you around the fireplace. His "as if" approach in reading aloud made people think of him as a great public speaker.

---

* From James F. Bender, "How to Master the Art of Reading Speeches," *Sales Management, The Marketing Magazine* (March 20, 1959), p. 112, p. 115. Reprinted by permission of the publisher and author.

Now the two chief aims of the sales executive who wants to be a skillful oral reader are:

1. *To make the matter easy for his audience to understand.*

2. *To hold the attention of his audience.*

When you achieve these two aims, you need not fear boring others with your reading. In face-to-face situations, your reading is both pleasant to the ear and eye of the listener. Surveys indicate that audiences prefer to listen to excellent readers than to poor public speakers. Incidentally, one of the best ways to become an excellent public speaker is to master first the art of reading aloud.

TWELVE SUGGESTIONS

Let's assume you have paid little attention to the technique of reading aloud. How much time will you have to spend to master the 12 suggestions that follow? Two weeks—if you have no unusual sight or speech handicaps. But you must practice at least 15 minutes a day for each of the 14 days; preferably, the same time every day, such as after dinner. (Certainly, a stingy price for such a useful—and for many —a most valuable skill!)

So, let's turn to 12 suggestions to become a skillful oral reader. You may want to use the suggestions simply to check up on your present oral reading habits. Or, you can use them to train yourself to read aloud in a masterful way—starting from scratch.

1. *Read the matter silently before you read it aloud.* Make sure you know the meaning and pronunciation of every word. If you don't, consult a good dictionary. As you grow in skill

in reading aloud, you won't have to read the matter silently beforehand. In the beginning, it's necessary to do so. Later on, optional—depending on your skill and confidence.

2. *Read from a standing position first.* Stand tall; chest high—to lift it off the diaphragm for easy breathing; hands at sides between gestures.

3. *Put your reading matter on a lectern.* If you don't have one, here's an idea for a useful makeshift: Turn a wastepaper basket upside-down on a desk or table. It comes to just about the right height.

4. *Practice before a mirror—large as possible.* A full-length mirror is ideal. If you practice in your bedroom you may have a full-length mirror on your closet door. Put the table (with the upside-down waste basket) before it.

5. *Before you begin to read, appraise or survey your make-believe audience.* You do this by looking into the mirror. Let your eyes travel to encompass your entire audience. You do this to get attention; to establish your authority over the audience; to get set.

6. *Announce the title of what you're going to read as part of your introductory remarks.*

7. *Read communicatively.* This means glance up at your make-believe audience as often as you can. Favor a different part of the audience each time you glance up. This maintains your contact with everyone in the audience. It allows you to supplement your words with meaningful facial expression, too.

As you practice you'll notice that you'll look up increasingly often—and for longer periods. Reason, of course, is that your eye-span for phrases, clauses, and sentences will expand. This is very desirable. An audience of one or many gets bored with the reader who keeps his head down—his nose in the manuscript.

8. *Read conversationally, not in a wooden way.* Here a voice recorder is of great help. Your aim is to make the reading sound like talking. And so you'll vary your tempo and your voice—just as you do in lively conversation. If you read your own manuscript, write it in conversational style, with interjections, "your attitude," etc.

9. *Now take up your manuscript or book and—at the end of a paragraph—walk out from behind the lectern.* Stand still, survey the audience, and start to read again. (Don't hide your face with the reading material.) This is a bit of showmanship—a comfortable break for you and the audience too—especially if you're reading a long piece. (You can't do this, of course, if you're reading before a stationary microphone.)

10. *Keep your place in the reading matter so you won't lose it as you glance up.* One way to do this is to keep your thumb in the margin—opposite the line you're reading.

11. *Now, practice from a sitting position.* Look up at the audience in the mirror as you read. Assume again that you're reading to a committee or panel around a table. In the course of your reading, glance up at every member present—not in successive order; skip around as you do in a conversation circle.

12. *Mark up your manuscript to get the most out of it—to make it easy to read.* If it's a formal presentation you're reading, have it typed triplespaced, four spaces between paragraphs. Use capitals generously. Allow several spaces between sentences. Indicate pauses, special emphasis, even gestures. Use any indication to help you—colored markings, etc.

PREPARING AND SENDING THE MESSAGE 135

Here then, by practicing these 12 suggestions, is a way to read aloud well. Result, more personal confidence before an audience and added competence. When the sales executive reads aloud well at his own sales meeting, he provides his salesmen with a good model. They'll admire him for it.

Discussion and problems

1. Do you agree with Bender that "one of the best ways to become an excellent public speaker is to master first the art of reading aloud?" How much practice do you think it takes to become a skillful oral reader?
2. Bender lists twelve suggestions for reading speeches. Can you add any other suggestions that you have found helpful in reading a speech?
3. Bender's suggestions are aimed at sales executives speaking at sales meetings. Do you think his suggestions apply to other speakers, situations, and audiences?
4. Bender says that "if you read your own manuscript, write it in conversational style, with interjections, "your attitude," etc." Can you add other examples of conversational style? List additional suggestions for writing a manuscript that can be easily understood by an audience?
5. Write a twenty-minute technical speech to be read to a lay audience (uninformed about your subject, but intelligent), or give an oral reading of a published technical paper. Practice reading the speech, using Bender's twelve suggestions as guidelines. Evaluate the helpfulness of the author's suggestions.

3 SOME IMPORTANT SPEAKING SITUATIONS

Spartans, stoics, heroes, saints and gods use a short and positive speech.
RALPH WALDO EMERSON, *The Superlative*, 1847

The technical man in his daily professional life must face a variety of speaking responsibilities in addition to those of an engineer or scientist formally addressing an audience about his own work. He may be asked to chair a panel, committee, or a meeting in a technical organization or a civic group, and occasionally he may be asked to introduce and thank a speaker. Every professional man also must anticipate the possibility of delivering a short impromptu speech with little or no notice. Within his own company or corporation, an engineer spends a great deal of time in giving informal oral reports to managers who must evaluate the information in order to make decisions. If an engineer or scientist is an executive, he is expected to give company speeches which explain company policies and promote public good will. All of these situations involve speaking skills and all are important because they help to insure the successful functioning of groups and organizations. The four articles which follow suggest helpful procedures for meeting these important and difficult challenges.

How to chair a committee and a technical meeting *

E. J. Tangerman, technical editor and consulting engineer, is a member of the Department of Planning and Development, McGraw-Hill Publications. The two articles reprinted here were part of a periodical series on speaking by the author which appeared during 1959 and again in 1965. Engineers and scientists are often asked to chair a panel or committee, and to coordinate speakers and speeches at technical meetings. Both of these functions are important to the success of any technical or professional organization. The practical advice offered by Tangerman is briefly but pointedly stated.

Chairing the Panel and Committee

PLANNING

Panels, symposiums, conferences, and committee meetings share one common characteristic—they're too long. The fault is usually with the chairman, who fails to establish and enforce an agenda, a schedule, and time limits. And he fails to recognize all participants equally and impartially, even if they were picked by a program committee without his help.

---

* From E. J. Tangerman, "7 Steps to Better Oral Reporting: *6 . . . Chairing the Committee or Panel," *Product Engineering* (September 27, 1965), p. 71. "7 Steps to Better Oral Reporting: *7 . . . How to Chair a Technical Meeting," *Product Engineering* (October 11, 1965), p. 125. Reprinted by permission of the publisher and author.

PANELS

Here the duty of the chair is to introduce the subject to the audience, to describe the ground rules, to introduce each speaker, to accept and distribute questions from the floor, and to sum up the presentation when it is completed. He is expected to settle any debates or arguments and to smooth any ruffled feelings. It is also his duty to subdivide the general topic by panelists and to assign each an appropriate share of the time.

Contrary to general impression, the successful panel discussion is not simply as many presentations as there are panelists (four is fine, six the top limit). While an individual may speak for 30 minutes, or even an hour, the individual panelist should preferably speak for 5, or at most 10 minutes, and the rest of the period be taken up by an interchange of remarks and comments. The symposium is simply a more formal panel discussion, in which speakers usually have prepared papers and represent divergent points of view. (Better get copies of prepared statements, so you know *in advance* how much time they'll take.) If the audience is permitted to ask questions, it becomes a forum.

COMMITTEES

The usual technical committee (please—not over 10 to 12 people) is a function of its chairman—it stands or falls on his ability. Remember that committees are formed to interchange information, to collect information, to judge an idea or action, to advise another person or body (even the chairman), or to inform. Be sure of what the objective is before you start, and be sure the committee is properly constituted —avoid deadwood and men with fixed minds. The chairman should in most cases not be the expert as well, because he cannot maintain order or interest if he is doing *all* the talking; he must, however, have the authority. And the chairman must also make the initial decision: Should the meeting be held at all? Would a memo, a circular letter, a ballot, or a decision by the chairman save everybody time?

The chairman is also the order-keeper who maintains discipline, keeps the discussion relevant, stops arguments, abuse, facetiousness. He obviously grants the floor to a speaker, limits debate and speaking time, avoids partiality by granting the floor to all sides equally and recognizing new speakers when possible. He puts a question to vote and announces the result. He relinquishes the chair if he presents any discussion himself.

GROUP THINKING

Essential in any problem solving conference is reflective, considered thought, as distinct from random or "closed-mind" thinking. Remember that the committee conference is slow and costly, so should be used only when there is a problem to be solved worth the cost. It offers the advantages of group knowledge, providing it is an honest group, with neither closed minds nor insufficient knowledge (pooled ignorance is still ignorance). Finally, John Dewey gives these steps in reflective thinking: (1) awareness of the problem, (2) analysis, (3) determining tentative solutions, (4) examination of solutions, (5) choosing one solution and trying it, and (6) verifying the solution.

PHYSICAL ARRANGEMENTS

Be sure the physical arrangements are suitable—that, in a panel session, the panelists sit high enough to be seen, that each is readily identifiable, that amplifying facilities are adequate. The committee or conference group usually sits in an oval or rectangle, preferably around a table on which paper and pencils are provided. Each conferee should be able to see and hear *all* the others. Most important, don't fail to be sure all are invited, know the time and place well in advance—check your men just before to be sure they remember.

SKILLS OF THE CHAIRMAN

The successful panel or committee chairman is a straight, fast thinker, an easy and offhand speaker, capable of straightening out the language of the others to their satisfaction, a good analyst, fair, tactful, and patient. He must be able to get others to talk and not talk too much himself, must avoid setting himself up as an expert or a judge, must exercise control and proper direction through cooperation. He must be skilled at giving the topic interest and value in his introductory remarks, then unobtrusively sliding out of anything but the directing and controlling function. He should be able to ask questions that build the pooled information, that encourage the reticent member to speak up.

THE VICE-CHAIRMAN OR SECRETARY

It is advisable to have a vice-chairman or secretary. He is *not* an ornament. He handles written discussions, reads abstracts for those authors who are not present, notes extemporaneous discussions which should be available in writing, prepares a report of the meeting or session, notes attendance, helps with visual aids. He can also evaluate discussions as they are presented. Most national societies have folders of instructions for speakers, chairmen, and aides.

Chairing a Technical Meeting

Masterminding a meeting is *not* just presiding, shining, and introducing each speaker or subject with a flourish. It includes a number of responsibilities, some beforehand, if the meeting is to achieve anything like its potential.

PROGRAM

Plan a coordinated program for a series of meetings or the individual meeting. Experiment with meeting procedures until you find the most successful one for the particular group, then stick it out. For success: Start and stop on time; avoid those tiresome committee reports when there's nothing to report or complete minutes of the previous meeting; don't bog down the meeting by introducing committee members, old-timers still active, and minor visitors, by allowing pep talks by officers and egotistical biographical reports disguised as "coffee talks." Most technical meetings suffer from too many "papers," poorly prepared and delivered, about subjects of too-limited interest—and worse, actually disguised puffs for speaker or company product.

BEFORE THE MEETING

Prepare a schedule showing events, approximate times, and any *bons mots* you just can't resist. Have biographical data on your speaker and condense it. Don't plan to read it in complete detail or to abstract as you read. Don't be flowery. Be sure you can pronounce the speaker's name and any biographical details you use, such as Greek-letter societies. Know what the speaker plans to say so your introduction doesn't digest or anticipate him.

Know whether he needs a blackboard and pointer, projector (type and size) and screen, easel, podium, or other accessories; and check in advance for power outlets and details of operation. A frequent missing link is the extension cord for the projector. Try the microphone and projector, the latter for focus and visibility, the former for position and adjustment as well as distortion. If there are to be reporters present, or the speech is to be taped or stenotyped, be sure the speaker knows of it. And be sure the microphone is readily adjustable, podium and projector lights are independent of general lighting circuits, and someone who knows is at the controls.

CARE AND FEEDING OF SPEAKERS

Unless his subject is so important nobody cares, be sure the speaker can speak, and tell him well in advance what you want him to cover and in what time. Tell him about how big his audience will be, whether or not ladies will be present, what the special audience interests and peculiarities are. If there are other events or speakers, tell him what they are and where he fits. And if you plan interviews, radio, or TV coverage, warn him.

Check even local speakers a day in advance to be sure they know time and place and how to contact you quickly if they need help. Meet an out-of-town speaker at train or airport and take him to his hotel, so he will feel he knows someone in your group. Reserve his room. Better still, invite him to lunch (if it's to be an evening meeting) with several of your officials and offer to arrange and conduct plant visits for him. Check your introduction with him, and warn him if blue stories are not approved. Arrange signals for more voice and for time limits. If he has brought his wife, delegate wives from your group to offer her help and entertainment.

DISCUSSION

If the paper or speech is to be followed by discussion, prime at least two friends to ask questions (not the unctuous types who ask rhetorical questions or deliver flowery compliments). Decide whether you or the speaker will handle the question period and if questions are to be oral or written. Written questions are usually slow and awkward, except in very large meetings (more than 200) where there is danger that the question will not be heard. Have discussors identify themselves *first*; it's only fair. Sum up the discussion points in your closing remarks, unless the speaker does.

AFTER THE SPEECH

Be sure the speaker has transportation to hotel or airport. Thank him in person, and write him a thank-you note later, enclosing clippings of press coverage.

WHEN AND WHAT TO PAY

Most speakers at technical meetings are covered for expenses by their employers. However, college professors, consultants, and military personnel may not be and may expect expenses at least. If your meeting is outside the field of your speaker's employer, either in geography or in market, he may not be able to charge expenses. And he may be making some part of his living by speechmaking. So state in your first contact with him what your policy is. Post-speech presents are appreciated, but should be of nominal value.

EMERGENCIES

As chairman, you'd better have an alternate program in mind in case your speaker is ill or doesn't arrive—a stand-in speaker or an industrial movie. Your job is the occasional drunk, too-persistent heckler, long-winded questioner, or floor orator. The first step is to remonstrate, the second to demand quiet, the third is physical removal. Do you have a couple of bouncers? A sort of emergency is the speaker who can't stop. Just stand up, or walk toward the podium. Only the hard-shell speaker will misread your intent. Should windows be opened or closed, corridor doors closed, kitchen help or people in the hall outside cautioned to be quiet? That's part of your responsibilities, too, through your aides.

Discussion and problems

1. What does Tangerman believe to be wrong with most panel and committee meetings?
2. What is an ideal number of panel members? length of each presentation? How should part of a panel discussion be spent?
3. What are some of the functions that a committee can serve? Why is it necessary to determine the objective of a committee before calling a meeting?
4. How might it be helpful if the chairman of a committee discussion is not the expert on the topic being discussed? Can you think of situations in which it might be advisable for the chairman to be an expert on the topic being discussed? How and when might he express his expert opinion?
5. What are the advantages of a committee conference called to solve a problem?
6. Explain the reflective thinking or problem solving technique used in committee conferences which attempt to solve problems. Should scientists and engineers already be familiar with this technique?
7. Describe the duties and skills of a good panel and committee chairman. Do you think any of the skills can be learned? What are some of the duties of a chairman's assistant (vice-chairman, secretary, or recorder)?
8. Arrange a classroom panel discussion (consisting of a chairman and four or five panel members) on a topic of current scien-

tific or technical interest (e.g., how science can help to solve the problem of famine; the causes and effects of air and water pollution; the feasibility of using solar energy; etc.). The chairman should carry out all the duties described by Tangerman, such as subdivide the general topic by panelists, announce the subject to the audience, introduce each speaker, set time limits and allow for interchange of remarks, distribute questions from the floor (the rest of the class), and sum up the presentation. Assign a class member to critique the effectiveness of the chairman. Evaluate the overall effectiveness of the panel, and offer suggestions for improvement.

9 Arrange a problem solving conference in your class (consisting of a chairman, a recorder, and four or five conference members) on a problem of current technical or scientific interest (e.g., decreasing fatal injuries to passenger car drivers; legalization of narcotics; the kinds of public transportation carriers and systems needed for the future; etc.). The chairman should carry out all of the duties described by Tangerman. For additional help in assigning and carrying out responsibilities, all participants (chairman, recorder, and members) should refer to Appendix D (Checklist for Planning and Conducting a Committee Conference). Evaluate the results of the conference.. How well did the conference follow the reflective thinking or problem solving technique described by Tangerman?

10 How would you sum up Tangerman's advice to the chairman of a technical meeting? Why are all the practical points mentioned by Tangerman so important?

11 Write several technical or scientific organizations asking for printed copies of instructions to chairmen of technical meetings, or arrange an interview with an engineer or scientist who has chaired a technical meeting (consult with your instructor about possible sources of information). Give a ten-minute oral report on what you learn from your correspondence or interview.

Three hard speeches to make [*]

George McWilliam has worked as personnel assistant and head of industrial safety for the British Columbia Hydro and Power Authority, Victoria, British Columbia. He has also taught and organized courses in public speaking. Technical people who actively participate in professional and public meetings need practice in delivering impromptu's, introductions, and thank-you's. The formulas offered by McWilliam do not necessarily guarantee a successful performance, but they do provide suggestions that every speaker can build on.

The Impromptu Speech

There's little doubt that one of the hardest speeches to make is the impromptu speech where you have very little or no time to prepare exactly what you want to say. Two other kinds of talks which can give you some difficulty unless handled just right are the one you give to introduce another speaker and your comments following his address. However, there are certain rules you can follow which will make all three much easier for you. But let's take them one at a time!

An impromptu talk is a speech that you may be called upon to deliver entirely without notice to an expectant audience. To the novice this could be a terrifying experience and this type of situation probably more than any other, has persuaded people to study public speaking. The favorite

---

[*] From George McWilliam, "Three Hard Speeches to Make," *Petroleum Refiner* (October 1959), pp. 225-227. Copyright by Gulf Publishing Co., 1959. Reprinted by permission of the publisher and author.

theme in some magazine advertisements for teaching public speaking by correspondence has been, "The president asked me to speak at the sales convention and three months later I was sales manager." However, joking side, a well made, thoughtful impromptu talk has undoubtedly been the turning point in many careers.

At the outset, let us say there is nothing to be afraid of. We will take for granted that you know the subject of your speech. You know something of it or otherwise you would not have been asked to speak in the first place. However, you have been asked—now, how are you going to do it?

YOUR BIG CHANCE

The big secret of this type of speech is simple organization. Whoever has asked you to speak knows you have some particular knowledge of the subject. Another point in your favor is that your audience knows you are on the spot and is sympathetic. The most important thing now is what impression are you going to give them as you rise to your feet. Are you going to "er" and "ah"? Will you apologize—say that on this short notice—stall and confound the friendly confidence of your audience at the outset? If you are, opportunity has pounded on your front door and pitched a tent, but your answer has been a rebuff. No, you can't do that!

You should smilingly address the chair, and your audience quietly. Pause to allow your audience to relax, then start off with a standard introduction. You must give an impression of poise, sincerity, and possibly specialized information.

Now, as to the technique peculiar to the impromptu speech. The average audience believes it to be difficult but with your knowledge of public speaking you know it isn't.

SOME IMPORTANT SPEAKING SITUATIONS 149

USE THIS FORMULA

The easy formula that has been a key factor in the speeches of nine-tenths of the impromptu speeches ever made, is contained in the following seven words:

1. What
2. Where
3. How
4. Why
5. When
6. Who
7. Which

Your thoughts and knowledge can be compared to a flowing stream containing thousands of units of useful but unharnessed energy. These words can be compared with power stations that transform your knowledge into power to perform useful work and provoke action.

They are questions you ask yourself about the subject although not necessarily in the order named.

For instance if the subject was unemployment:

HOW has employment been handled in this country?
WHAT governments have handled it?
WHAT has it cost?
WHERE has unemployment been concentrated?
WHERE has trouble developed?
WHY has trouble developed?
WHO have been unemployed—young or old—male or female?
WHEN did it start?
WHEN will it end?
HOW can it be ended in your opinion?
WHICH is the best method of handling it?

STUDY OTHERS

You can see from the formula using those seven words that it is very easy to develop a talk on very short notice. You will find in your impromptu speeches, you will benefit from carefully studying other speakers. Little tricks that they have used, and that you have unconsciously observed, will come to mind and assist you in the construction of the speech.

Some speakers frequently called on for impromptu speeches have a store of anecdotes or quotations suitable for almost all occasions: "Ladies and gentlemen, the prime consideration at this moment is brevity—my remarks therefore will be like a modern feminine costume—long enough to cover and short enough to be interesting." However, while such tricks are not essential, they have their value.

The essentials are contained in the formula given above. Do not drag out your speech. Have a thought provoking introduction and directly you have said what you have to say put a punch into your conclusion and sit down.

It is well to remember that an impromptu speech is an opportunity. Accept it. Take it seriously. It's quite simple.

The Speech of Introduction

In introducing a speaker yours is a two-fold task. First, you must make your speaker, your guest of honor, feel at home. Secondly, you must introduce him, efficiently and graciously, to your meeting.

In making this introduction your prime consideration is brevity. The situation, embarrassing and annoying to both speaker and audience wherein the chairman makes an address of some length introducing a speaker, is a landmark of humor. However, it definitely is not humorous. I can recall several cases where a chairman has taken over thirty minutes to introduce a speaker.

RULE ONE—BE BRIEF

In preparing a speech of introduction, and a speech of introduction must be prepared just as any other speech, there are two angles to consider:

1. The material for your speech.
2. Your manner of delivery.

Let's take these one at a time. The material for your speech of introduction should include:

1. What is the subject?
2. Why is the subject?
3. Who is the speaker (not necessarily his name, but what he is)?
4. Why is he the speaker?
5. Appreciation of courtesy of the speaker.
6. Welcome and formal introduction.

The above could be a formula for a "safe" introduction—brief, thoughtful, and gracious. Here's how it works in actual practice.

Your job is to secure the attention of the audience for your guest and naturally you have prepared for the task. You possibly have telephoned his secretary for certain information asking her if there is any particular angle that should be stressed. You may have contacted him directly. If he is a well known person, you have possibly contacted the better known sources such as your public library.

ONE EXAMPLE

Let us use the formula and develop a short introduction:

1. *What is the subject?* "Today we are to be favored with an address on unemployment."

2. *Why the subject?* "This is without doubt one of the outstanding problems of our country. You will hear it discussed North and South and East and West—in high places and in low. It is the subject of gossip and deep concern. We all have our pet solutions for the problem. You all have come in personal contact with it and it must affect directly and indirectly the livelihood and future of every one of you."

3. *Who is the speaker?* "If anyone can be called an expert and authority on unemployment, our guest today must certainly be placed in that category. For years Secretary of Labor, he has come in contact with almost every phase of the problem. Since his college days when he worked his way through Yale University, he has seen this problem grow in national significance."

4. *Why the speaker?* "His studies and experiments in the field of unemployment have been watched with close interest across the entire United States."

5. *Appreciation.* "I know that his courtesy in honoring our table today is appreciated by you all."

6. *Formal Introduction.* "Gentlemen—the Honorable _____ secretary of labor, who will address you on the subject of unemployment—Mr. _____."

The above is only one application of the formula. There are many, many, varieties of application.

BE CAREFUL

One warning, in preparing your material: be sure that it is accurate. If you are not sure of its accuracy, throw it out.

Never take a chance if you want to avoid embarrassing yourself and your meeting.

One more warning—this may seem absurd to you, but be sure to get the name of the speaker correctly, and its correct pronunciation. This situation is not so extreme as you may surmise—it does develop quite occasionally and because of the regularity of its development it also is firmly ensconced in the field of humor. You have probably heard before of the chairman heaping praise on praise—"he needs no introduction, Mr. er .... ah .... er."
Therefore:

Print his name somewhere where you can see it plainly from your standing position when making the introduction.

The speech of introduction is a prepared speech. The ordinary rules of speech construction apply. The speech has an introduction, body, and ending. As you grow in experience you will introduce your speech of introduction with an anecdote or a humorous note. You will refer to previous associations with the speaker and so on. However, until you have more experience play it safe. Stick to the formula. Your job is not to impress your audience with your wit—it is to introduce the speaker.

WHAT MANNER?

As far as manner is concerned, this is most important. A chairman, ill at ease (possibly because he has not prepared his introduction) will make his audience restless and will handicap the speaker before he commences. Relax—smile. Genial and urbane is the ideal chairman. Your speech of introduction is not a declamation but delivered if possible in the conversational style.

Your job once again is to create a receptive atmosphere and make your guest feel at home.

An important part of your speech is the indication or the cue you give your guest that he now has the floor. Just before finally using his name, turn to the guest speaker and with a slight bow and possibly a gesture—invite him to his feet. *Remain standing until your guest commences to rise.*

The "Thank You" Speech

Over a period of time you have all heard speeches of "Thank You." You will all agree that a brief, gracious speech of "Thank You" can add considerably to your program.

Let's briefly delve into the mechanics of it.

Unless this is a response to a toast, this is always an impromptu speech and you have rules for impromptu speeches in this article. One thing that must be remembered is that you are responding on behalf of the meeting and you should indicate this in your remarks quite plainly. Often the speaker is addressed directly.

BE BRIEF

All that is really required is tact and courtesy. Brevity again is the first criterion. I am often reminded of the old saying "Take the bull by the horns." In the case of thanking a speaker I suggest you take "the bull by the tail." You can let go just that much sooner.

If there is such a thing as a formula for a speech of "Thank You" it most certainly should include the following:

1. A reference to the chairman's introduction.
2. A reference to a highlight of the speech.

3. Thanks for his courtesy in attending.
4. If he calls for action assure him that his representations will receive consideration.

Here is a sample of a short "Thank You Speech."

Mr. Chairman, Mr. _____, Gentlemen. It has fallen to my privilege to express on your behalf, our sincere appreciation of Mr. _____'s address. We have keenly anticipated this talk because there is not one of us that is not familiar in some way with the very fine work in the field of unemployment research of our honored guest. In his address today he has opened new vistas of thought for us.

His figures on the problem have astounded all of us, and I know that I can assure him on your behalf that his suggestions will receive serious and immediate attention.

Mr. _____, the applause of this meeting has indicated to you in a small measure our appreciation of your most thoughtful address and too—of your courtesy in visiting us. It is all too seldom we have the opportunity of listening to so thoroughly informative an address.

Thank you, Sir, and may we extend to you our best wishes for your continued success in your work on this problem—Unemployment.

KEEP IT SIMPLE

Once again—you are still a novice. You are not unique in this category as 75 percent of our speakers are in the same classification. However, your audience need not know this and they won't know it as long as you do not attempt to over-elaborate your speech. Make it *simple, brief,* and *courteous.*

A simple, brief speech will be appreciated by the speaker and will adequately express the thanks of the other listeners to the address.

Alternatively, an over-elaborate speech will stamp you for what you are and will be the reverse of your object—to thank the speaker for his address.

There are probably very few better ways of developing executive qualities in employees than through public speaking. Although all can't be leaders, public speaking aids in developing confidence and poise which sometimes is so necessary for promotion.

Discussion and problems

1. How does McWilliam define an impromptu speech?
2. What impression should an impromptu speaker give an audience?
3. What is the one key to a successful impromptu speech? Explain McWilliam's formula for a successful impromptu speech. Add to the formula by listing points that you have learned from good impromptu speakers (for example, a brief mention by the speaker of how the topic affects the daily lives of the *audience*).
4. Using McWilliam's formula as a guideline plus your own observations of good impromptu speakers, give a five-minute impromptu speech to your class on a topic selected by your instructor or a classmate who knows your interests.
5. What two tasks are involved in introducing a speaker? What is the prime consideration in introducing a speaker? What do you think an appropriate length for an introduction?
6. What three adjectives does McWilliam use to describe a "safe" introduction? Explain his formula for a "safe" introduction. Can you suggest other possible material for a formal introduction?
7. What warnings does McWilliam add to his advice on introducing a speaker? Can you think of other warnings?
8. How would you describe the proper manner of delivering an introduction?
9. Prepare a two- to three-minute formal introduction of one of your classmates who is giving a speech to your class. How did you apply McWilliam's formula?

SOME IMPORTANT SPEAKING SITUATIONS   157

10 Why is a "thank you" speech expresing gratitude to a speaker an impromptu speech situation?
11 What does McWilliam believe to be the first criterion of a "thank you" speech. What three adjectives does he use to describe an effective "thank you" speech?
12 What is the effect of an over-elaborate "thank you" speech?
13 Explain the author's formula for a "thank you" speech, and add any elements that you have found to be successful.
14 Give a two-minute thank-you speech after one of your classmates has delivered a speech in class. To what extent was McWilliam's advice helpful?
15 How does public speaking practice help in making the "three hard speeches" described by the author?

Oral reports to decision makers *

Roswell Atwood has taught courses in the art of communication for thirty years, including special courses and seminars for upper management and trade union leadership. Dr. Atwood's article is concerned chiefly with how engineers or employees with detailed knowledge of a matter should select and organize information for managers who must use it to make a decision. The future of many research projects has undoubtedly been affected by the competence with which an engineer or scientist can communicate ideas to upper management.

KNOWLEDGE AND DECISION

To clear the air for preparation of a top-notch oral report, we must first understand what it is. Basically, it is a verbal statement of fact from one who has detailed knowledge of a matter, but not the responsibility for decision, to one who has the responsibility for decision but who lacks detailed knowledge. When we consider the oral report, we confine our thinking to the transfer of the statement of fact by talking.

KINDS OF ORAL REPORTS

There are two kinds of oral reports. One is the regular type and the other the special type. Regular reports keep

---

* From Roswell Atwood, "How to Sell Your Ideas Orally," *Petroleum Refiner* (December 1960), pp. 126-128. Copyright by Gulf Publishing Co., 1960. Reprinted by permission of the publisher and author.

supervisors informed of progress on matters they have assigned to others. Such communications are brief and informal. The informality tends to prevent realization of their importance, as, indeed, is true of other types of informal talking.

The first requirement of a report, regardless of its type or purpose, is orderliness. Ideas must be in natural sequence—that is, one thought must lead coherently to the next. In most regular reports there is a similar content, brief mention being made of those things that are going well and more detailed reference being given to the troubled areas.

PARTS TO THE ORAL REPORT

There are five parts to the well-ordered oral report, whether regular or special. These are:

1. Preliminary
2. Statement of Fact
3. Induction from the Fact
4. Subsidiary Remarks
5. Conclusion

These five parts are essential to orderly presentation and have been so regarded for many centuries. The preliminary is the opening statement. The necessity for the report, or its significance, or its relation to what has previously been done or said, is stated here. The length of this part of the report depends on the situation, ranging from the very brief to one which is comprehensive and extended.

In any event, say what is necessary in order to establish relationships. The statement of fact contains the basic material of the report. It is the longest part, so it must be complete without being verbose. Such detail as is required is included. The listener may not want to know every fact in detail; therefore your approach will be in accordance with his desires as you know them to be.

Up to this time the report has been factual only. Induction from the facts given is the next step. This is the logical reference that may be drawn from the facts. Care must be taken that there is an obvious relation between the facts as given and the inference reached. It is in this part of the report that many people fail. They do not show the logical relationship with what has been stated as factual. It is vital to success in this type of talking that you think of your report, as much as you can, from the point of view of the listener.

Subsidiary remarks provide a further opportunity to relate the facts and the induction. This is often effectively done by using visual aids.

The conclusion is the summary of the report. A common fault in reports is to state a series of facts and then present conclusions which have no apparent relation, or very little relation, to those facts. This is especially a failing in regular oral reports. In such a procedure, the listener must ask several questions in order to get the needed information. This could easily cause the supervisor to doubt the ability of the man reporting.

Regular reports offer opportunity for demonstrating the detailed knowledge of what is being done, the ability to think clearly and concisely, and the quality of brevity.

KNOW YOUR LISTENER

The ability to report effectively doesn't just happen, nor does it occur as a result of concentrating on reports. Talking with others is the result of mental attitude toward what takes place under any talking situation. It is essential that we think about what we say as we say it.

Listening to oneself is as vital as listening to others. We must think about those who are listening to us, especially considering whether the words we use will have a similar meaning for him as they do for us. When the subject of the report is technical, such concern is extremely important.

The regular report is usually expressed in conversational terms. The main difficulty is to emphasize the important items without combining matters that should be kept apart. This distinguishes oral reports from conversation, although the general approach is the same as far as formality is concerned.

It is easy to talk too much. Condensation is required in any report, and selection is one of the most troublesome aspects of such talking. Your selection should be based on the amount of detailed knowledge that your listener has and the significance of each item to an understanding of the whole situation. Anything which does not contribute to these two points should be omitted.

THE SPECIAL REPORT

As more responsibility is reached, there are more special reports to be made. Such reports concern investigating ideas and plans and describing results of research. These are more formal in structure than the regular reports. They are more carefully planned, visual aids usually being employed, and rehearsal frequently is necessary.

A special report requires full notes, in considerable detail, but not the reading of these notes verbatim. Accuracy in factual statement calls for care and deliberation. For this reason the special report takes time in preparation.

VISUAL AIDS

Authorities agree that the special report should be assisted by visual aids. This is true because people understand more readily and retain longer what they see than what they hear. The combination of hearing and seeing is the ideal for both understanding and retention, provided that the talker plans carefully and delivers well. Planning the visual aids includes careful selection, making sure that whatever is used is large enough. Restrict the number of such aids so they do not become cumbersome. More reports have been ruined by too many visual aids than from any other cause.

If charts are to be used, the combination of color becomes important. For best visibility most people prefer black lettering on a white background. Dark green lettering might also be used. Avoid such combinations as light red on a green background. Make the letters or figures large enough to be easily seen. Many times the omission of this precaution has meant failure of the listeners in a group to follow the report. Often the ineffective chart results in additional questions and some confusion. Thus, it may detract rather than add to your presentation.

Slides may be used to supplement the spoken word. Their advantage is that they can be projected in sufficient size to meet the needs of a large number of listeners. The same precaution should be observed as to lettering or figures being big enough to be seen.

HANDOUTS

If mimeographed or printed material is to be used, distribute it at the time when it will be effective. This is when you want to direct attention to specific portions of the printed material. If listeners are given such material when they enter the room or when you begin your presentation, many of them will look through the various items, reading what most interests them. They will not hear what you say.

By waiting for distribution until you can use the material as an aid, you will increase the effectiveness of delivery. The best time to hand out your mimeographed aid is during the fourth part of the report—subsidiary remarks. Of course, this cannot always be done when the nature of the report requires an early visual supplement.

The maximum understanding and retention occurs when people read the words while they hear them. The most significant points in the report can be indicated, then read while the listeners follow by reading as well as hearing.

Again, be careful in the use of visual aids. It is a temptation to employ too many of them, so that they lose much of their effectiveness. Assure yourself that the use of something for people to see will really promote understanding. If there is any question about such a device, don't use it.

VERBAL CONTENT

Most of a special report consists of the statement of facts. These must be presented objectively, without personal opinion and feeling. State the facts as you find them to be, leaving out all your own opinions. Many managers become very suspicious of the report that is colored by feeling. They will sometimes decide contrary to what may be sound recommendation because of the introduction of personal feeling in the report.

A special report has conclusions, and these must be definite. Conclusions must be the logical result of the factual statements previously made. Present the findings explicitly, briefly, and with a manner that suggests sound judgment. If your relationship is such with the man or group receiving the report as to make it helpful, your opinion can be added to the report as a separate item, clearly indicated.

Skill in making reports is an asset to any engineer or supervisor. The same concern for the listener ought to mark all talking, without regard to the formality of the situation. We can only talk as well as our habits permit us to do and this should lead us to the resolve that we will really become aware of what we say and how we say it—all the time.

Discussion and problems

1. How does Atwood define the oral report and its purpose? How does this stipulative definition affect his remarks on the organization and content of the oral report?
2. What is the difference between regular and special oral reports? Why are both important? What is the first requirement of both?
3. Explain what goes into the five major parts of a well-ordered oral report, regular or special, and why each part is important. What does Atwood mean by "induction from the fact"? Give some examples.
4. From what point of view should a speaker consider his oral report to be given a decision maker? Why?
5. What problems of giving an oral report are discussed under the section "Know Your Listener"? Can you think of others?
6. How can visual aids and handouts help an engineer in giving an oral report to a supervisor? When and how should handouts be used?
7. What advice does Atwood give about presenting the facts in an oral report? Under what circumstances and where should personal opinions be expressed in an oral report?
8. Atwood concludes by stating that "skill in making oral reports is an asset to any engineer or supervisor." Explain.

9 Carefully prepare and informally deliver a ten-minute oral report, using the organization and advice given by Atwood. Assume that you are an engineer or scientist who has been thinking and working on a project that your supervisor must evaluate (for example, deciding if, how, when, or where the project should be used or continued). Be sure to think through the exact purpose of your oral report and the amount and kind of information needed by your supervisor (you must also judge your supervisor's technical sophistication). Plan to use one visual aid or one handout.

The modern executive as speechmaker *

Many engineers and scientists who become part time or full time executives in a corporation find that they often are asked to give speeches designed to explain corporate policies and activities and to promote public good will. In such situations the engineering executive is not explaining his own research or specialty, but rather he is serving as a spokesman for the organization to which he belongs. The practices and problems of executive speechmaking were discussed in a management newsletter section of **Electrical World**, *and are reprinted below. Some readers may be surprised to learn that many companies are vitally concerned with promoting successful executive speeches.*

SPEECH AS A MANAGEMENT TOOL

Bored by dull, lifeless rhetoric, and uninspired by platitudes and cliches, the speech listener will hastily offer that most executive speeches are poor. Take this beleaguered listener, however, invite him to the podium, and chances are his harangue will also cause as much attention as a stalk of corn dying in Kansas.

It's no secret that most speeches accomplish little more than exercising the speaker's vocal chords. Even the public relation men who assist in preparing speeches know that the oratorical efforts of executives are often a waste of time, according to a study made by Opinion Research Corp, Prince-

---

* From "After the Convention . . . Was that Speech Worth the Effort," *Electrical World* (March 7, 1966), pp. 75-78. Reprinted by permission of the publisher.

SOME IMPORTANT SPEAKING SITUATIONS 167

ton, N.J. ORC's survey of some 50 PR directors and another dozen PR consultants shows that over half (52%) rate the other fellows' speeches as "poor."

Ideally, a speech can be an excellent tool for management —it can boost company prestige, and promote public understanding of corporate policy. ORC reports that both PR directors and outside consultants maintain that a good speech can produce five distinct benefits: (1) give the company positive visibility through the person of a top executive; (2) provide leadership position as a spokesman for the industry; (3) publicize a message hard to get across in any other way; (4) dispel misunderstandings about company activity; and (5) persuade others that the company has intelligent and enlightened views on such issues as civil rights, automation, the role of government.

Skeptics might argue that while these are noble aims for any company, even a good speech delivered to a group of groggy conventioneers leaves few lasting impressions. Not so. A wide secondary distribution of speeches is often more important than reaching the immediate audience, says ORC.

Most companies which are conscious of the benefits which can be gained from the dais concentrate on getting multiple impact from speeches, via press coverage and reprints. And the majority of corporations concede that the secondary audience is the most important.

Some companies naturally are more successful with their speech efforts than others, and ORC investigated to see just what it was these companies were doing right. The criteria which ORC set up in order to find which companies were leaders in speechmaking included: citation by other companies; whether they take the initiative to find a platform when they have something important to say; and whether they have established procedures for coordinating the development of top executive speeches.

By separating the men from the boys, ORC probed into the actual practices of the leader companies in speechmaking, and found that there were at least seven practices common to all. Let's examine each, starting with the phone call inviting an executive to make an address.

LEADING COMPANIES SCREEN SPEAKING INVITATIONS

Leader companies have firm criteria for accepting or rejecting invitations to speak. First of all, the executive must have something significant to say at the time. The audience must also be important enough to warrant his delivering a speech, to help insure wide distribution of the message via press coverage. Finally, the speech must come at a suitable time, so as not to disrupt the executive's over-all plan for appearances, resulting in over-exposure. Executives are encouraged to say "no" when they should.

Speeches given by executives of leader companies are geared to meet important company objectives. However, this planning should be flexible, as unexpected issues or problems may arise that provide the company with opportunities to speak out on themes not contemplated in advance. In general, however, thematic guidelines should be established. The public relations director of a leading oil company expressed it this way: "We believe speechmaking would be futile, a mere wheel-spinning exercise, if we didn't have a pretty good idea in advance of what we wanted to say."

Overexposure of speakers is a danger carefully avoided by leader companies, and almost all feel that chief executives should not go to the rostrum more than four or five times a year. As one public relations director explains it, "The top executive is like a piece of valuable currency. You don't want to cheapen it by too frequent use."

There should be a limit, too, on the length of an executive's speech. Among the practitioners interviewed in the ORC study, most thought that major speeches shouldn't exceed 20 or 25 minutes. Longer speeches are likely to bore the audience, while shorter ones rarely do the topic justice. Exceptions might be seminar appearances or college lectures. The speaker with an established reputation is badgered with requests each year. Some receive anywhere from 50 to 150 invitations annually. But the executives who have yet to make the grade as speakers face the opposite problem—finding important forums.

Leader companies may advise these aspiring orators to do one or more of the following, in order to get into the limelight: select a subject important to the company in which the executive has interest or expertise, then have the executive write articles for trade, industrial, and other publications on that subject; conduct seminars on the topic; and for beginning forums, informally seek out speaking invitations from small or local organizations.

A good speech requires extensive research, but few executives have time for doing the research themselves. Leader companies make extensive use of writers and researchers, who work closely with the man delivering the speech. While a few executives (about 15%) in leader companies insist on preparing their own speeches, most speeches are the result of joint effort.

EXECUTIVES SHOULD USE WRITER'S SKILLS

"The executive and the writer have to know each other well and be able to work as a team," says one PR director. "The executive saturates the writer with his point of view on the subject." In this way the executive utilizes the craftsmanship of his assistants, but this does not mean the executive is not expressing his own point of view.

Poor delivery of a speech can mar its effectiveness, and the sad truth is that many executives do a mediocre job of getting their message across. Their delivery often lacks expression, rhythm, and emphasis. Leader companies try to minimize this defect by having the executives take lessons in speech delivery before they take to the rostrum.

Also, they will see to it that the language of the speech is comfortable to the speaker, and that he delivers the speech with a personal style, perhaps ad libbing, or injecting some humor. The less experienced executives should rehearse extensively before delivery, say leader companies.

"Many executives simply haven't taken the time to learn how to speak well," advises one PR consultant. "This is really a pity since it is not that difficult. I've seen some really poor speakers become vigorous and dynamic on the platform through experience and training."

TOO MANY REPRINTS BRING DIMINISHING RETURNS

While the use of reprints is an effective way of reaching the secondary audience, they must be distributed selectively in order to receive the best reception. Reprints have more chance of being read, says ORC, if they are restricted to the most important executive statements; if they are attractive in format; and, if they are distributed only to those who have reason to be interested in the subject.

When properly utilized, however, reprints can have impact. ORC cites the example of one large company which has a highly selective, well-planned reprint program. "Thought leaders" who regularly receive the company's reprints were asked if they read the reprints. About 70% said that they usually read them. Of these, 70% admitted that they learn something new from the reprints. In addition, a special test showed that opinion of the company became more favorable when people were exposed to reprints.

Companies should not duck controversial issues, points out ORC. Leader companies report that executives should take the initiative in speaking out on such matters as automation, civil rights, government interference, the causes of unemployment. "Sure, many executives will talk about subjects that are considered 'controversial'," says the president of a leading PR consulting firm, "but they will do so in such a way as not to displease anyone—not customers, not stockholders, not dealers, not employees. The results are bland, really meaningless statements. And very few of course, are willing to challenge orthodox business views."

EXEC'S CHOOSE GUTSY THEMES, BUT DON'T FOLLOW THROUGH

While it is generally agreed that many executive speeches are of poor quality, ORC decided to have 25 executive speeches diagnosed by a communications specialist, to determine exactly what is wrong with so many speeches. It was found that executives do a good job in selecting themes for speeches, but often fail to argue their cases convincingly. Specifically, this failure to follow through is due to one or all of the following six classical errors:

1. Insufficient documentation and illogical defense of key points.
2. A blurring of the main points through lack of fresh ideas.
3. Vague and generalized talking about a theme.
4. Conclusions that are too strong or do not follow from the data given.

5. Extreme statements of a position, usually associated with attacks of varying violence on the opposing position.
6. Concepts that are so jumbled or unexplained as to be virtually meaningless.

Executive speeches are strong on cohesion and simplicity of language, but weak on organiation and clarity, found the communications expert. While the speeches are generally well put together and ordered in some logical way, the structural organization—the balance among the parts, the use of "echo" and arguing from the general to the particular to the general—was often weak. And despite the simplicity of the words used, the meaning of many of the speeches was obscure, fuzzy, unclear.

PUNCHY PROSE SHOULD REPLACE SOPORIFIC UTTERANCES

The most notable flaw of all in the speech was the flat, uninspired language. It seems that executives are reluctant to use lively prose. Dry, spiritless language in dreary succession is the rule: fresh, colorful language the exception. The result is dullness, a sad fact realized by anyone who has ever sat through a series of speeches.

Dead copy is not inevitable, however, regardless of the speech topic. The writing of lively copy is not especially difficult—what is needed is proper awareness by the executive, points out the expert. If he wants to be eloquent, or if he is afraid that a colorful mode of discourse might harm him, chances are the speech will be stale.

Fear of being flippant or unstable is suggested as the reason why more executives don't employ colorful language in their speeches. Yet there are numerous examples of phrases which are memorable only because of the manner of expression, where images have been used to light up a concept.

"The absence of elegance and color is regrettable," concludes the specialist, "particularly when the substance is not neglected. When an executive has struggled over the content and really has something to say, it hurts not to say it well. Saying something well helps make memorable that which is well to say."

Discussion and problems

1 Explain the five distinct benefits of a good speech listed by public relations directors and outside consultants. Can you think of other benefits to a company or corporaiton? to a speaker?
2 Explain the importance of secondary audiences in corporate speechmaking?
3 What criteria did Opinion Research Corporation (ORC) use to find which companies were leaders in speechmaking? What seven practices were common to all leading companies? Do you think that these practices are advantageous to both the company and the speaker?
4 What help does a company often provide an executive in writing and delivering his speech? To what extent do you feel that such help can benefit an inexperienced speaker? Why must "the language of the speech be comfortable to the speaker"?
5 How do reprints of important speeches and statements help a company?
6 How forcefully do you think that a company executive should speak out on controversial issues of public interest?
7 Explain the faults of twenty-five executive speeches diagnosed by a communications specialist. From your own experience, can you give specific examples of the faults listed? What advice would you give an executive speechmaker to help eliminate these faults?
8 What is meant by the term "punchy prose"? When is it important in a speaking situation? How can a speaker replace flat, uninspired prose with lively prose?
9 Imagine that you are the president of a corporation. Give a ten-minute speech to your executives explaining how to give an effective company speech.

4 ELECTRONIC MEDIA/
Aids for seeing and hearing technical data

There's a lot of difference between say-so and take-a-look.
AMERICAN PROVERB

A technical speaker, regardless of the subject of his speech or the type of audience and occasion, often finds that he can more effectively present and explain his message by using audiovisual aids. These aids are what Marshall McLuhan has called electronic extensions of man's senses. They are means of extending, stimulating, and reinforcing sensory impressions. All of us live in an age of visual stimulation, and psychologists have long pointed out that we learn more through the eye than the ear, that we learn faster through the eye than the ear, and perhaps most important, that we remember more if we both hear *and* see. But audiovisual aids *per se* are not sure guarantees to successful technical speaking or learning and in the hands of naive speakers can bore or confuse an audience. If a technical speaker is to effectively plan and use aids such as slides and overhead projectors, closed-circuit television, or even a microphone, he needs rules or guidelines. The articles which follow, based on the experience of technical speakers, present such rules. Because slides and transparencies are a favorite means among engineers and scientists for projecting and discussing technical data organized into graphs, tables, equations, and diagrams, the art of designing and talking about slides is frequently emphasized. Topics covered in other articles include closed-circuit television for demonstrations, speaking effectively with a microphone, and increasing information exchange with an overhead projector. The advice offered in these articles is not intended to make the technical man an audiovisual expert, but rather to help him become more skillful in conveying his message with audiovisual aids as well as words.

A complaint about speakers and slides *

Harold G. Lorsch is a research engineer and manager at the Missile and Space Division, General Electric Company, Philadelphia, Pa. Like so many engineers and scientists, Dr. Lorsch has sat through a number of professional meetings in which the speaker left his audience in the dark, literally as well as figuratively. The following comments and suggestions on papers presented at meetings of engineering societies appeared as an open letter of complaint to a journal editor. The complaints are particularly aimed at those speakers who feel that visual aids can carry a talk regardless of their content or manner of presentation.

LISTENING IN THE DARK

During the past 10 or 15 years, ever since the majority of the papers presented at meetings of engineering societies became the result of organized, sponsored research rather than individual sparetime efforts, the presentation of papers has become more elaborate, more formal, more visual than oral, and—unfortunately, in too many cases—less interesting. This is not to say that the technical level of the papers has deteriorated, for quite the contrary is true. The manner of presentation, however, is no longer geared to a listener, but to a reader instead.

---

* From Harold G. Lorsch, "Presenting a Paper? Here's How," *Mechanical Engineering* (March 1961), p. 94. Reprinted by permission of the publisher and author.

For example, at the 1961 ASME Winter Annual Meeting, like at similar meetings of ASME and other engineering societies, I sat through interminable hours in dark rooms being lulled to sleep by the monotonous soliloquy of the speaker. He had trouble reading his lecture notes in the dark which was relieved by a single bulb illuminating the speaker's chin rather than his manuscript. He was running back and forth between the screen and the lectern, and the sound would fade in and out as he was approaching or going away from the microphone. Three-quarters of the audience were asleep, and the remainder were awake because (1) they had just had a strong cup of coffee, (2) they were talking to their neighbors, (3) they were getting up to leave the room, (4) they were speakers scheduled to follow the present speaker and did not want to miss their cues, (5) they were chairing the meeting and valiantly tried, sometimes unsuccessfully, to stay awake.

The speaker did not have the slightest inkling that three-quarters of his audience were asleep since the darkness made it impossible for him to communicate with his audience effectively. At the end of his talk the lights would go on; this and the applause of the few awake members of the audience would briefly rouse the slumbering majority. They did not have to stay awake for long, though, since the next speaker swiftly had the lights turned off after the first few sentences of his talk.

This description may strike some people as either humorous or exaggerated but, unfortunately, it is neither. If the considerable expense in time and money on the part of the Society and the attendees at these conventions is considered, this method of transmitting technical information at meetings seems highly inefficient.

SUGGESTIONS

The following suggestions are made with the intent of improving the communication between speaker and audience and thereby increasing the usefulness of technical lectures.

1. *Remember that you are delivering a "talk," not a "paper."* By presenting your work in person you undertake the responsibility of communicating verbally with your listeners. Therefore, do not read your formal written paper to them. They can all read.

2. *Look at your audience.* Any radio or TV actor can tell you how difficult it is to speak to an unseen audience. You do not have to work under this handicap if you keep the lights on throughout your lecture room and stay away from the distractions of the projection screen which forces you to turn away from your audience.

3. *Keep the number of slides to a minimum.* Slides should not be used for giving an outline of your talk, for boring your audience with the intricacies of mathematical derivations, or for presenting a wealth of test data.

If a great many data are significant, they should be digested at the reader's leisure and not within a fraction of a minute during which they are flashed on the projection screen. If there are only a few significant data, what is wrong with giving them verbally? Not all of us have lost the ability to absorb the spoken word.

If the details of the mathematics are really interesting, they deserve more study than can be given on the screen. If you want to outline the method only, the spoken word is far more effective in doing that than a bunch of equations thrown at an audience unfamiliar with them.

4. *If you have to, use few, simple slides.* Slides are suitable for showing entire structures, complicated pieces of

equipment, and for the comparison of data, i.e., graphs. Their judicious use can greatly enhance the value and understanding of a talk. But remember, the slides are an auxiliary to your talk, and not vice versa. Do not let your talk become a commentary on your slides.

5. *Leave the lights on while you show the slides.* This is the easiest remedy for the worst drawback of most current talks. A suitable, simple slide shows a clear photograph or a plot drawn with heavy lines accompanied by a minimum of text. Such a slide, properly prepared, can be seen clearly with most projection equipment if the lights in the room are kept on at normal strength or slightly dimmed. By keeping the room lighted you avoid losing your listeners through darkness-induced slumber. You maintain contact with them by being able to see and talk to them as individuals rather than an amorphous mass somewhere beyond you in the dark.

Next time you give a talk, try these few simple rules, and you will be surprised at the difference which the presence of a live, wide-awake audience makes on your presentation.

Discussion and problems

1 Why does Lorsch believe it is important that a speaker should deliver a "talk" and not a "paper"? look at his audience?
2 In the author's opinion, what information should not be put on slides? Can you think of other subject matter that need not be presented on slides?
3 Do you agree that the "number of slides be kept to a minimum" and that the "talk not become a commentary on your slides"? Explain.
4 What information does Lorsch believe to be suitable for slide presentation? What information do you think appropriate for slide presentation? Give examples.
5 Why is Lorsch so concerned about proper lighting?
6 What is the main point of the author's five suggestions?

7 Can you suggest how a speaker using slides might avoid "running back and forth betwen the screen and the lectern"?
8 Prepare a fifteen-minute technical talk in which you do one of the following: (1) describe a complicated piece of equipment; (2) describe a complex process; or (3) present and interpret data (e.g., the number of passenger car vs. airline fatalities during the last ten years). Prepare four or five simple slides to help you in your talk. Explain what criteria you used in deciding on what information to put on the slides.

Lantern slides and such: how to cope with data and slides *

J. R. Van Pelt *is President Emeritus of Michigan Technological University. His criticisms concerning visual aids provide classical advice, particularly for those engineers and scientists who design and use slides showing tables and graphs. The often humorous tone of the article does not suggest that the author takes his subject lightly. Rather his description of Dr. Brown's misfortunes and Whiffle's syndrome helps to underscore acute observations on the misuse of visual aids. The remedies are prescriptions for avoiding what Dr. Pelt calls an "occupational disease."*

HOW TO LOSE AN AUDIENCE

The chairman finished his introduction, and the principal speaker, Dr. Demosthenes Brown, stepped to the microphone. With skill born of long platform experience, he quickly gained the interest and confidence of the audience. His voice could be heard clearly, even back under the balcony. His eyes seemed to meet those of every listener. His whole dynamic personality was projected to every corner of the room.

Soon Dr. Brown was ready to get into the meat of his talk. It involved complex numerical data, so he had decided to use some lantern slides—a new undertaking for him. To ensure accuracy, he had personally prepared the material for the slides. Today, before the session started, he had

---

* From J. R. Van Pelt, "Lantern Slides and Such," *American Scientist* (July 1950), pp. 450-455. Reprinted by permission of the publisher and author. Based upon an article in the *Quarterly Journal of Speech*, 36, February 1950.

checked with the operator of the projector to make sure that everything was in readiness. Now, at a well-timed signal, the room lights were turned off.

In the resulting darkness, Dr. Brown and the audience lost sight of each other. This was something he had not anticipated; somehow he had overlooked the fact that "eye contact" depends on on visibility. In an effort to regain the ground thus lost, he raised his voice and put a little more life in it. This ought to have helped. But unfortunately, at that instant Dr. Brown turned away from the microphone to look at the image on the screen, and his amplified voice faded pathetically away. The good Doctor was annoyed with himself for making this elementary blunder, but he had no time to dwell on it, for this is what he saw on the screen:

Year	Average number of men at work on each scheduled working day	Total number of man-days worked	Total man-hours worked, based on net working time	Total man-hours worked, based on total time in the mine ('portal-to-portal' time)	Number of fatal injuries incurred while at work	Number of non-fatal injuries (lost time accidents only)
1930	493,202	92,325,875	750,149,205	850,326,612	1,619	71,217
1931	450,274	73,349,461	595,979,561	674,845,333	1,080	53,975
1932	406,380	59,259,624	479,447,331	452,160,523	958	39,352
1933	418,752	69,881,999	564,425,166	638,100,656	833	43,946
1934	458,044	81,647,939	591,058,597	677,087,424	958	46,982
1935	462,354	82,291,724	578,511,200	665,019,499	968	47,529
1936	482,500	95,261,754	669,900,536	769,787,050	1,098	50,514
1937	490,771	96,130,313	675,568,195	776,548,688	1,198	52,847
1938	445,246	71,747,050	505,316,161	579,723,732	880	36,794
1939	445,044	78,966,259	554,984,350	636,802,063	867	38,544
1940	440,847	88,770,852	625,973,555	717,970,096	1,204	43,994
1941	457,744	97,999,557	691,049,388	791,396,491	1,072	46,637
1942	448,797	109,491,371	772,828,992	883,483,050	1,245	53,193
1943	407,135	106,911,764	777,970,318	883,675,272	1,225	51,067
1944	376,203	104,705,401	883,770,709	914,925,290	1,124	51,253
1945*	363,000	94,750,000	762,000,000	841,000,000	936	47,750
1946*	380,000	83,900,000	670,000,000	730,000,000	800	44,000

*Preliminary data, subject to revision
Number of Men Employed, Total Man-Hours of Exposure, and Number of Fatal and Non-Fatal Injuries in Bitumious-Coal Mines (Including Strip Mines) in the United States, 1930–1946 Inclusive.

Dr. Brown paused in some dismay. Somehow the typing looked smaller than he had expected. Was the screen too small? No; he quickly realized that the trouble was with the slide.

"I'm sorry, ladies and gentlemen," he heard himself saying, "that this slide is so hard to read. But the figures are important, so I'll read them to you." Someone called "Focus!" The operator twiddled the focusing screw; the image blurred, then jumped into focus momentarily, then blurred again. Half a dozen helpful people called "There you are!" or "Hold it!"—but the operator (who, it seemed, was slightly nearsighted) turned the screw a little too far. As the jockeying continued, Dr. Brown tried to read the slide aloud. But it was too late; he had lost his audience. Instead of a unified and interested group, he had on his hands some apathetic people, some impatient ones, a few kibitzers near the projector, and a great many who had suddenly decided to converse audibly with their neighbors. Dr. Brown's heart sank as he realized that, because of a few apparently trivial details, he was "flubbing" an important speech.

The further misfortunes of the eminent Dr. Brown with his newly made slides need not detain us; for other speakers have re-enacted them on a thousand platforms until they are well—too well—known to us all. We have seen over-crowded slides projected by machines that could not be focused. We have watched while speakers in a large room tried to use maps or charts that could not be read beyond arm's length. We have listened in vain as able scholars talked confidentially to a blackboard while writing illegible symbols with invisible chalk. We have fidgeted, mentally if not physically, as the remarks of a renowned scientist came to a dead stop while he adjusted some ill-arranged piece of apparatus or hunted for a scientific specimen to illustrate his point.

AN OCCUPATIONAL DISEASE

The habit of badly using bad visual aids is rampant among those who "speak to inform." It is an occupational disease of university professors. Severe epidemics break out at every scientific, engineering, and medical convention. Someone has said that the hoof-and-mouth disease sometimes spreads to other species; and when it does, it is often complicated by a heavy incidence of Whiffle's syndrome.

Whiffle is an organic chemist. He became so famous for his researches that every chemists' club wanted him to come and tell them the story. At the first few meetings of this kind, he just spoke. Then it occured to him that diagrams of some of his big organic molecules would look impressive, so he had some slides made. In the slides, each atom in the molecule was shown by means of a small circle; lines connecting the circles showed how they were bonded together. That was fine at first, but as his research continued, he developed bigger and bigger molecules. To get them on a lantern slide, he had to make the scale of the drawings smaller and smaller. By the time the molecules got up to a few thousand atoms, the circles got so small that they looked like the dots of a halftone engraving. Whiffle thought the slides seemed a trifle crowded, but he was busy, so he has been using them ever since.

Whiffle also wanted to show some of the smaller molecules in three dimensions. He couldn't do this on the screen, so he built cagelike models of the molecules out of wooden balls and stiff wire. With the balls and wire painted in different colors to represent different kinds of atoms and bonds, they were very impressive, although it must be admitted that Whiffle displayed them more as a curiosity than as vital, concrete support for his talk. The audiences always duly admired the workmanship, but only one person ever asked any questions about the models. That was the young son of one presiding officer who brought the boy along when the baby-sitter failed to show up. The boy's question was whether Whiffle didn't think they would make good cages for squirrels.

As time went on, other symptoms began to appear in Whiffle's talks—such as standing in front of what he had written on the blackboard, or passing around so many specimens that half the people in the audience would be busy handling them. Those readers who wish to investigate the full array of symptoms included in Whiffle's syndrome are referred to the exhaustive descriptions that have appeared in the journals devoted to abnormal psychology. Briefly, the symptoms all stem from Whiffle's apparent belief that visual aids automatically ensure interest, understanding, and conviction.

At a recent meeting of some five hundred engineers at the Waldorf, a well-known consulting engineer showed a lantern slide with 120 lines of tabulated figures. Even though the screen was extra-large, the typing was so small that the speaker couldn't read it even from his position right by the screen. He finally read most if it from his copy on the lectern—a process that consumed about ten minutes. The slide retaliated appropriately by cracking in the heat.

USABLE PRINCIPLES

Professional societies and similar groups have been so plagued by such performances that several of them have prepared booklets or articles of instructions on the design and use of visual aids [1], [2], [3]. These instructions are fine for the serious student of Whiffle's syndrome, or for the man who wants to make a lifework of lantern slides and such. But for you and me, who prepare visual-aid material only once in a long time, they're just too complicated. What we need are some simple, usable principles that we can apply without recourse to higher mathematics.

Let's say that you are scheduled to give a talk next month on a rather technical subject. The technical material might be economic or social statistics, or it might be data on physical or chemical properties of some material, or possibly the structure of something from a molecule to a skyscraper. Whatever it is, you have decided that you can convey such data more successfully by a combined appeal to eye and ear than by the spoken word alone. You have outlined your talk, and you have made marginal notes indicating tentatively what slides you think you will need.

As you expand your outline into final form—either notes for extempore speech or a formal paper written out in full—you assign a title and number to each slide. You find that a few more slides are needed in one spot, but, if you are wise, you may also find several slides that don't carry their weight. You see that they are excursions into nonessential detail, so you cut them out. You check your speech to see that each slide will have at least half a minute on the screen. If you feel that perhaps there are too many slides for the time at your disposal, you ruthlessly cut the number down. You also ponder any situation that calls for keeping one slide on the screen more than three or four minutes.

PRESENTING THE DATA

Now you are ready to design slide No. 1 This is where Dr. Brown fell down. To avoid similar mishaps, you are going to work out the design of each slide, together with your oral comments on it, as a study in the psychology of communication.

Data can be presented in many forms. You can use tables, as Dr. Brown did, or you can use graphic devices. Graphs are preferred when the data permit, i.e., when they show systematic trends, patterns, or comparisons. Also, graphic presentation is obviously applicable where the information is concrete and picturable, like the crystalline structure of an alloy, the shape of a bacillus, or the appearance and dimensions of a mechanical part. If, like Dr. Brown, you were speaking on industrial health and safety, you might use the data in his first slide, but you would put most or all of it in graphic form instead of in numbers, and you would use three or four slides instead of one.

Before you start to make the graph for your slide No. 1, you might want to take a quick look at some of the standard works on graphic presentation of data [4], [5], [6], [7]. You will find them full of fascinating detail. However, if your time is limited, you may postpone that and get along with the few pointers that follow.

LETTERING AND SPACING

It is a good idea to fill the screen comfortably with the slide image. A long, narrow field, either vertical or horizontal, looks awkward on the screen and is seldom necessary. To avoid such slides, adjust your copy to fit in a space 10 units wide by 7 units high. These figures are close to the proportions of most screens, and also near the proportions of the openings in standard slide mats, both the 2 X 2-inch and the 3-1/4 X 4-inch size.*

Make a rough pencil draft of the chart on a piece of plain paper. Begin by drawing a 10 X 7-inch rectangle, and then fit the data into that space with due regard for margins, legibility, and your best guess as to how the eye can be guided to see what you most want seen. Then explain the slide aloud

---

* Editor's Footnote—Although screens currently used are often square rather than rectangular and although many speakers now use 2X2-inch color slides, the author's concrete advice on lettering and spacing graphic devices still applies to the design of slides that are readable and aesthetically pleasing. It can also be applied to the lettering and spacing of graphic devices shown on transparencies with an overhead projector. To prepare a transparency, for an overhead projector with a 10X10-inch aperture, adjust your copy to fit into a rectangle no larger than 9 inches wide and 7 inches high.

as though to an audience. Delete every unnecessary word; in most slides cut out the title, since that is covered by the spoken context. The audience can read only 10 to 20 words without losing the speaker's thread of thought.

How big should the lettering be? On your 10 X 7-inch original, never use any lettering less than 1/8 of an inch high; 3/16 of an inch is better. If your draftsman uses lettering guides, those numbered 140 (meaning that the letters are 0.140 inch high) should be the smallest used.

Although typing is not so clear and attractive as good hand lettering, you may sometimes be forced to type the lettering on your graphs. When that happens, select a good typewriter, clean the type thoroughly, use a well-inked black fabric ribbon (or a carbon ribbon if you can get one), and draw the graph in a smaller rectangle. Later in this article you will find suggested sizes of rectangles for both pica and elite machines (10 and 12 spaces per inch respectively).

You may find, as you design the slide, that you are trying to cover several ideas in one slide. If so, divide them. Put only one central idea on each slide; additional material distracts attention. While you are talking about the first point, the audience races ahead and speculates about the others.

KINDS OF GRAPHIC DEVICES

For many kinds of numerical data, you will have to decide among curves, bar charts, pictographs, pie diagrams, and other devices. In general, curves are suitable for an audience of specialists, bar charts for practically any audience, and pictographs for audiences requiring some popular touch.

If you use curves on a background of coordinates, space the coordinates rather far apart; a grid of many lines makes an unattractive slide, and rarely does an audience really need to read a curve with high accuracy. Trends rather than precise quantities are usually discussed.

The pictograph, in its usual form, is a modification of the bar chart, using a row of pictorial symbols instead of a bar. Each symbol represents a given quantity, and the pictorial quality often helps to explain the chart with a minimum of text. Though not new by any means, its real popularity in this country dates from 1930 when the Chicago Museum of Science and Industry used it on a large scale. The man who introduced the technique in Chicago has written an excellent manual on the subject [8].

Pie diagrams are popular and they have some legitimate uses. But they are relatively hard to read with much accuracy. Bad pie diagrams are almost as common as bad restaurant pies. If you insist on cooking up a pie diagram, better read Marshall and Karsten, already referred to [5], [6].

If your object is to mislead, don't overlook the potentialities of the perspective diagram. You wish to exaggerate the increased tonnage of our naval vessels without actually lying about it? Say the tonnage today is eight times what it was at a certain earlier date. In a bar chart, you simply make the second bar eight times as long as the first. It tells the truth. In an honest pictograph, you would draw one little battleship for the first year and eight for today—all the same size. This also tells the truth. If you want to exaggerate a little, you can draw two similar silhouettes of battleships, the first one inch long and the second eight inches long. Now you're beginning to mislead your audience, for the second battleship occupies 64 times as much area as the first. If you want to go all-out for exaggeration, use two battleships in perspective instead of in silhouette, still keeping the first one inch long and the second eight inches long. Now the larger drawing looks like a ship weighing 512 times as much as the first.

You can juggle the figures even more by tampering with the perspective—but at this point let us draw the veil on this type of deceit. If you're an honest citizen, you'll never use a lantern slide of the type described, at least not without careful explanation.

TABLES

You may have to present some material in tabular form, as in Dr. Brown's first slide. But you don't have to make his errors in design.* You can use briefer headings. Where two or more columns deal with similar data, you can tie them together with a general heading, and use very short subheadings for each. You can use guide lines or double spacing to help the eye to follow an item across the table. And you can limit each slide to one central idea.

Perhaps the commonest error, in tabular data, is to make the lettering too small. Your typist, left to her own devices, may space the data so as to fill a whole page, just as she would for a typed manuscript. To avoid this, all you need to do is tell her the size of the rectangle into which the copy (with small margins on all four sides) must fit. With typical projection conditions, your audience will have trouble read-

---

* Author's Footnote—When Dr. Brown designed his slide he made at least nine errors of judgment. Errors are: (1) Too many points on one slide. He presented a mass of raw data that could make at least 10 slides, of which perhaps three or four were essential to his talk. (2) Column headings too wordy. Even if we retain all the columns, the headings could be cut from 52 words to 14. (3) Columns 4 and 5 should have a group heading and subheadings; also columns 6 and 7. (4) Figures should be rounded off to show trends, not details. (5) Footnote is redundant and, after rounding-off quantities, probably needless. (6) Title too long—seven words would do the work of 27; better yet, omit it entirely. (7) Proportions of slide are bad—about 10 to 4 instead of 10 to 7. (8) Too much space between columns; slide is nearly 150 spaces wide, and half of this space is wasted. (9) Horizontal guide lines or spaces needed at every third or fourth line. (10) Recast into graphs, preferably bar charts.

ing the slide if you crowd more than 60 characters and spaces into a line that runs clear across the screen. After allowing for right and left margins, you have 55 spaces left for a legible line of full width. Combine that with our 10-to-7 screen ratio, and we arrive at the following dimensions:

Elite type: a rectangle 5X3-½ inches allows space for 55 spaces per line and 18 single-spaced lines, plus a small margin all around.

Pica type: a rectangle 6X4-¼ inches allows 55 spaces per line and 22 single-spaced lines, plus small margins.

These dimensions make good, legible slides. In a pinch you can make the rectangle a little larger, but not safely beyond these top limits:

Elite type: 6-¼X4-⅜ inches; this gives 67 spaces and 23 lines, plus margins.

Pica type: 7-½X5-¼ inches; this provides 67 spaces and 28 lines, plus margins.

If you can't get your copy within these limits, you will do well to resort to surgery. Cut the data down somehow. Beyond this size, copy is likely to be both illegible and unduly complex.

All of these numbers sound confusing, but the essentials are easy to remember: *width*, 55 spaces; *ratio of width to height*, 10 to 7.*

Whatever you do, don't hand the photographer a big printed table and ask him to copy it. See that it conforms to the limits explained above. If it doesn't, it will be disappointing as a slide. Besides, if you rework the material you can usually improve the headings, round off the numbers, and otherwise adapt it to lantern-slide use.

---

* Editor's Footnote—If preparing a transparency of typewritten material for an overhead projector with a 10X10-inch aperture, keep all typed copy within a 9X7-inch rectangle. Do not try to put too much typed material on one transparency. Fewer words and bigger letters make the best transparencies.

SEEING EFFECTIVELY

Color photography and color drawings can be used to prepare lantern slides, even for charts and diagrams. Business statistics showing deficits in red could be photographed and thrown on the screen in black and red. Two curves on the same chart, shown for comparison, could be quickly distinguished by separate colors. Almost every conceivable slide contains some feature that could be brought out more effectively by the use of color.

Even after slides are well designed there are still many ways in which they can go wrong—as Dr. Brown found out. Why should the room be completely darkened for ordinary black-and-white graphs and tables? In a fully darkened room "eye contact" is lost, the audience cannot take notes, and latecomers cannot find seats. Complete darkness is desirable for pictorial slides but utterly unnecessary for graphs and tables. Before the meeting, turn out the lights closest to the screen and experiment until a satisfactory balance is achieved between room lighting and screen brightness; remember that visibility is not so good from the sides of the room as from the center.

A dozen other details will deserve attention from you or from a trusted assistant. You will want an unobtrusive signal system and a pointer—an electric pointer if the screen is very large. If a microphone is necessary, you may want the lapel type, to avoid being glued to one spot as you refer to the screen. You will certainly wish to adjust the light on the lectern so that it neither shines in the eyes of the audience nor causes too much reflected glow on the screen. You may even shield the corridor lights so that they cannot shine on the screen when the doors are opened by the people who take advantage of the darkness to sneak out in the middle of your talk.

GENERAL PRINCIPLES

So far we have discussed only lantern slides. Maybe you need some other device—wall charts, maps, blackboard, exhibits, lecture-demonstrations, or pre-printed data. We cannot discuss these in detail, though they certainly deserve it. But regardless of the type of visual aid you may use, certain principles apply both in the selection and the design of the material and in the use of it before an audience. Three such principles are these:

1. Visual aids are only aids. Make them reinforce rather than replace the spoken word.
2. Good visual aids focus rather than scatter attention. That, of course, precludes all irrelevant material, no matter how interesting.
3. Good visual aids must be visible, that is, clear and legible. Visibility depends in part on the design of the slide—content, arrangement, scale, color. These are all under your control; you alone are to blame if you fail to create a good design. Visibility also depends on the room—its lighting, the size and placement of the screen, etc. These also may be under your control, at least in part, if you take the trouble to investigate in advance.

References

1 *Engineering and Scientific Charts for Lantern Slides.* American Society of Mechanical Engineers. New York, 1932. Approved by American Standards Association, November 1932, and listed as ASA Recommended Practice Z15.1-1932. Includes short bibliography on graphic presentation of data up to 1932.
2 JORDAN, R. C., and EDWARDS, M. J. *Aids to Technical Writing*, Bulletin No. 21, University of Minesota Engineering Experiment Station. Minneapolis, 1944. Pp. 106-111.
3 BONNELL, L. S. "Preparation of Effective Lantern Slides." *Chemical and Engineering News*, September 12, 1949.

4 BRINTON, WILLIAM C. *Graphic Methods for Presenting Facts.* New York, 1914.
5 MARSHALL, W. C. *Graphical Methods.* New York, 1921.
6 KARSTEN, KARL. *Charts and Graphs.* New York, 1923.
7 ARKIN, HERBERT, and COLTON, R. R. *Graphs.* New York, 1936.
8 MODLEY, RUDOLF. *How to Use Pictorial Statistics.* New York, Harper 1936. Complete discussion of the pictograph technique; one short but useful chapter on other techniques. See also: "Facts Told Pictorially." *New York Times*, September 15, 1935.

Discussion and problems

1 Can you recall speeches similar to that given by Dr. Brown and Mr. Whiffle? Describe the situation and the audience reaction? Were you amused? Why does Van Pelt describe the situation humorously?
2 Why does the author describe the misuse of visual aids as an "occupational disease"? Do you agree that the "habit of badly using bad visual aids is rampant among those who 'speak to inform' "?
3 What misguided belief causes Whiffle's syndrome? What is the remedy?
4 What kinds of data are best presented in graphic devices? in tables? Give examples.
5 Aside from considerations of spacing and readability, why should the number of words and ideas be limited on each slide?
6 In Van Pelt's opinion what sorts of graphic devices are suitable for an audience of specialists? any audience? audiences requiring a popular touch? What specific advice does he give regarding the design of each of these graphic devices?
7 Illustrate with your own examples how a perspective diagram can exaggerate or distort data? Can the other graphic devices listed by the author be designed to exaggerate or distort data? Explain.
8 Using the corrective advice of the author, design new tables to be used for Dr. Brown's lantern slide. Contrast their effective-

ness with the old table. Recast the information in Dr. Brown's table into graphs for slide presentation. Which new slides do you consider to be the most effective—the tables or the graphs?

9 In what ways does Van Pelt believe slides can "go wrong" even after they are well designed? How can these mistakes be avoided?

10 What are Van Pelt's three principles of designing and using visual aids of all kinds? Can you suggest additional principles?

11 Prepare a twenty-minute speech on how to properly and improperly design and show slides (or transparancies for an overhead projector). To illustrate your main points, prepare slides incorporating tabular and graphical information.

12 Give a twenty-minute technical speech in which you show several slides (or transparancies) to help explain technical data and details. How did you decide which forms (tables, curves, bar charts, pictographs, pie diagrams) to use in presenting the data and details? List the principles which you used in designing and showing the slides? Can you supplement or modify the advice offered by Van Pelt?

Slides for technical talks *

The late O. E. Romig was Assistant Director of the Applied Research Laboratory, U.S. Steel Corporation. The main thesis of his article on slides for technical talks is that slides are used, not to confound the audience and use up time, but to help the hearer "follow, comprehend, and retain the idea expressed by the speaker." The article starts with eight general rules for preparing good slides; proceeds to give detailed instruction on tables, graphs, mathematical formulae, and flow diagrams; and closes with advice on the proper number and timing of slides and the use of color. An important corollary to the author's thesis is that every technical speaker, if he plans ahead, can produce and use slides that enhance his talk.

COMPREHENDING SLIDES

Good slides should help to put your technical talk over. Poor slides will almost surely put your audience to sleep. The graphs or figures published in technical papers are rarely suitable for use as slides, although they may be perfectly satisfactory for use in a published paper. The message or idea projected on the screen should be understood by the viewer almost immediately, whereas the published illustration can be studied for as long a time as is necessary to comprehend it.

The technical speaker often seems to believe that the purpose of a slide is simply to make his own job easier. Actu-

---

* From O. E. Romig, "Slides for Technical Talks," *Journal of Metals* (September 1962), pp. 632-634. Reprinted by permission of the publisher and U.S. Steel.

ally, a good slide will inevitably do just that. But if the speaker prepares a slide simply to cover up his own inability to express his ideas clearly, he may confuse the listener rather than help him to understand. The prime motive of the slide is to make it easier for the hearer to follow, comprehend, and retain the idea expressed by the speaker. Any speaker should be able to prepare good slides himself or have them prepared at a minimum of cost, if he will observe the following rules or hints.

RULES FOR PREPARING GOOD SLIDES

1. Attempt to convey one idea only, with clarity. Include only data pertinent to the one idea to be expressed.
2. Keep the subject matter simple. Remove all possible detail. Obtain close-up photographs rather than "cover the whole water front." Remember to show scale by including a human being or an object of known size.
3. Limit words or numbers to 15 or 20, if possible.
4. Letters and numbers must be large enough to be legible in the rear of the room or auditorium. The height of the smallest letter or number should be no less than $1/40$ of the height or $1/60$ of the length of the slide area. Use legible type or good clear lettering. The use of Leroy or Wrico guides is recommended in preference to hand lettering. If only a typewriter is available, it should have good clear type, such as the IBM electric executive models with carbon ribbon attachment instead of fabric ribbons. The amount of copy should be kept to the minimum and with adequate spacing. Remember the rule about minimum height of letters and numerals.
5. Avoid tables, if possible. Use graphs or charts instead. Use heavy lines because light lines may be lost in preparing the slide. Crosshatching, if used at all, should be simple.

6. Complicated ideas should be presented by the use of several slides.
7. All words and numbers should read horizontally.
8. The use of color adds greatly to the presentation.

Letter and Line Sizes Recommended for Superior Slide Appearance [1]

Copy Dimensions Margins Excluded [2] Inches		Leroy Templates & Pens [3] (Capital Letters)			Width of Ruled Lines		
Maximum Height	Maximum Width	Grid Notes Scale Captions	Sub-titles	Titles [4]	Light: Grid & Cross-hatching	Medium: Symbols & Flow Lines	Heavy: Curves & Important Lines
3-1/4	4-1/4	100-00	120-0	140-1	0.007	0.014	0.028
3-3/4	5	120-0	140-1	175-2	.010	.017	.035
4-1/2	6	140-1	175-2	200-2	.012	.021	.042
5-5/8	7-1/2	175-2	200-2	290-4	.014	.028	.055
6-3/8 [5]	8-1/2	200-2	240-3	290-4	.014	.028	.055
7-1/2	10	240-3	290-4	350-4	.017	.035	.069
9-1/2	12-1/2	290-4	350-4	425-5	.021	.042	.083
11-1/4	15	350-4	425-5	500	.021	.042	.083
12-3/4	17	425-5	500	700	0.028	0.055	0.110

1. These recommendations will give legible copy under adverse conditions, such as when the auditorium length is 9 times the width of the projected image (A/W = 9), and will give superior projected slide images under normal conditions. For example when the auditorium length is 6 times the width of the projected image (A/W = 6).
2. Copy size may be less in either direction than specified, but not in both dimensions simultaneously.
3. Recommendations given here are satisfactory for slides and for reduction to column width for use in publications having larger bold-face type, except as noted in (4) below.
4. Subtitles and titles may be lettered in the larger sizes specified here when they are desired for emphasis in slides. They will be too large and bold when the copy is to be used for printing in a technical publication. In publications, however, titles and subtitles are usually set in type below illustrations to match the format of the publication.
5. Preferred original size for general use it is convenient in size, easily filed, fits on standard 8-1/2 x 11 inch sheet with ample margins.

Figure 1. Published table, excellent for careful study, but not a good slide without condensation and elimination of much of the data.

TABLES

Compare Figures 1 and 2. Figure 1 is a published table from source material no. 4, very suitable for close study and reference, but it contains far too much information for a slide. Many speakers, however, attempt to present such tables as slides, much to the distress of the audience. Compare it with Fig. 2. a very simple table with numbers which can readily be seen and understood, even in the rear of a large auditorium.

EFFECT OF SPECIMEN CONDITION			
CONDITION	EXPOSED	FAILED	PER CENT
COLD WORKED, WELDED, STRESSED	61	37	60.6
COLD WORKED, STRESSED	22	12	54.5
STRESSED ONLY	78	33	42.5

Figure 2. Color slide from a black and white table produced by making two or three slide-size diazo transparencies.

Curves or bar diagrams are preferable to tables for presenting data in slide form. If a table is used, it should contain as few words and numbers as possible with a minimum

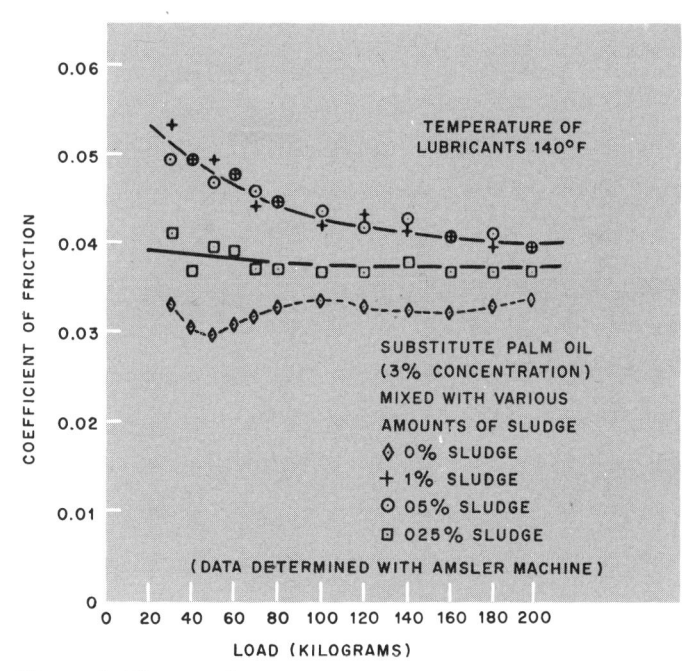

Figure 3. This graph prepared for technical publication is unsuitable for use as a slide.

number of digits. Abbreviations may be used, provided they are well known to the audience, or explained by the speaker. This may be better than spelling out long words and captions. Titles on slides are not usually necessary and, if used, should be very brief.

GRAPHS

Figure 3 is a rather simple graph prepared for a technical publication. In the writer's opinion, it is not good for use as a slide because it contains too much data and too many words. Furthermore, it does not fit a horizontal slide format, and the ordinate explanation reads vertically rather than horizontally. The ordinate in Figure 3 may be read when the reader is able to turn the printed page, but the slide viewer cannot turn the screen 90° in order to read.

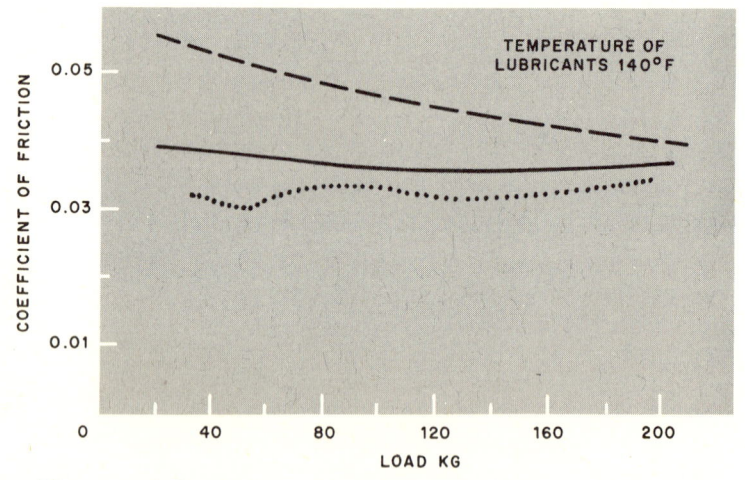

Figure 4. Color slide from 6x8-inch artwork showing the same idea as depicted in Figure 3 condensed for suitable slide presentation.

Figure 4 is a simplified version eliminating much data which may be explained by the speaker, if he sees fit to do so. In the three curves, it was necessary to present only trends and general position; therefore, points along the curves indicating individual determinations were omitted. From Figure 4, the audience can quickly grasp the meaning. Data points on which curves are based may be plotted on slides when pertinent to the spoken argument, but unless pertinent, they should be included only in the published version.

FORMULAE

If a speaker must present mathematical formulae by slides, the presentation should be simplified as much as pos-

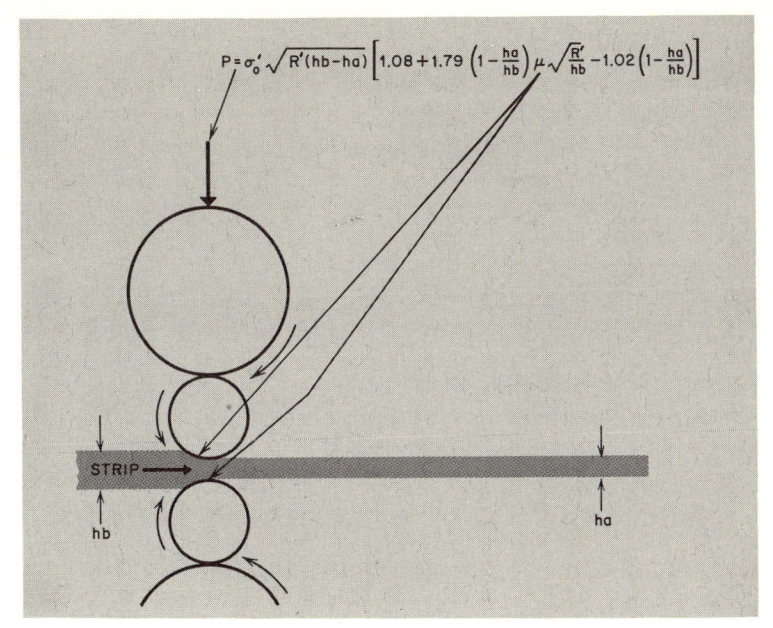

$$P = \sigma_0' \sqrt{R'(hb-ha)} \left[1.08 + 1.79 \left(1 - \frac{ha}{hb}\right) \mu \sqrt{\frac{R'}{hb}} - 1.02 \left(1 - \frac{ha}{hb}\right) \right]$$

Figure 5. Mathematical expression of coefficient of friction at work on roll and strip surface. Color slide prepared from diazo transparencies similar to Figures 2 and 4.

sible. Mathematical derivations or formulae should be shown so they are readable; this usually means presenting a maximum of one or, at most, two rather simple equations at one time. The symbols must be large enough to be read and should be neatly drawn (refer to rules 1, 2, 3, and 4). When a formula refers to a process, it may be clearly presented in a manner similar to Figure 5. This slide was made from art work, but it can be very suitably presented as a negative slide, with or without hand coloring. If the presentation of complicated mathematical derivations is necessary, it is preferable to hand out these formulae on a mimeographed sheet of paper to each member of the audience in order that the formulae may be studied thoroughly.

FLOW DIAGRAMS

Figure 6 was actually used as a slide several years ago! It shows the complete flow diagram of a process. The speaker was obliged to talk for several minutes to explain the various steps in the process. It might be suitable as an illustration for a technical paper, but it is not a good slide because

(a) Illustrating as it does numerous steps in the process, it attempts to convey too many ideas.

(b) The lettering is so small that the words and numbers would be illegible to a viewer seated in the rear of a fair-size room. In fact, the letters and numbers should be larger for use in a technical paper.

(c) The large white area of the background may cause eye strain to the viewer because of the glare of reflected light from the screen.

Figure 6 would have to be subdivided and presented as several separate slides in order to explain, satisfactorily, the

ELECTRONIC MEDIA 203

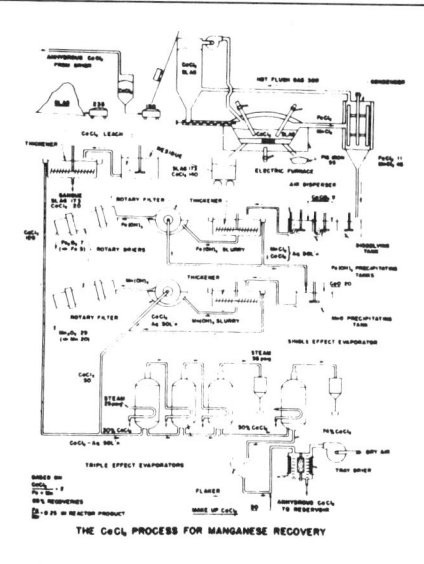

Figure 6. Complete flow diagram of a process, unsuitable for use as a slide.

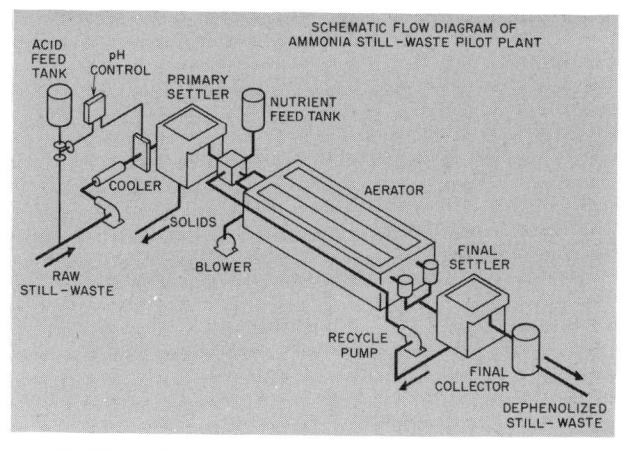

Figure 7. Flow diagram of maximum complexity for a good slide presentation.

individual operations of the process. Figure 7 illustrates about the limit of complexity for a slide of this nature. In fact, it really contains too many words as presented.

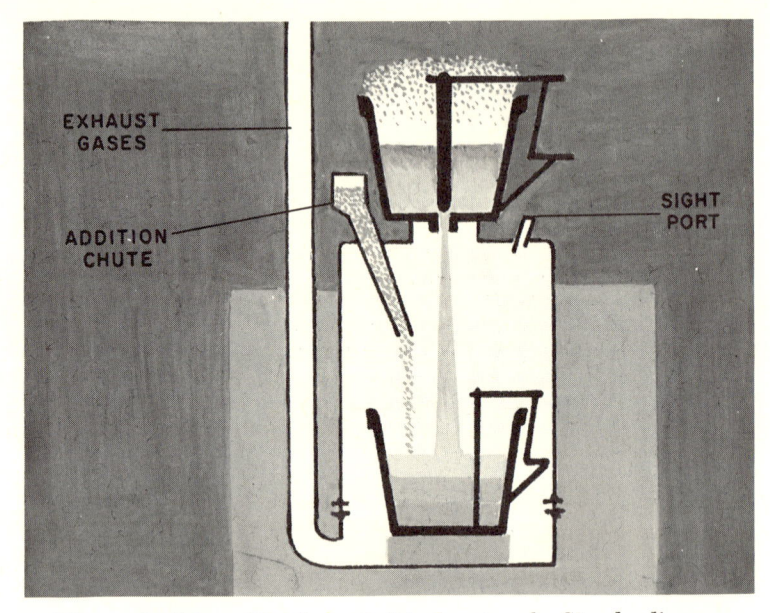

Figure 8. Color slide from 6x8-inch artwork. Simple diagram to illustrate the vacuum ladle degassing process for steel.

Figure 8 was prepared from full-color art work with a white overlay on clear acetate for words and arrows. This is very effective in color, and it is also satisfactory in black and white. The operation portrayed is simple enough to be understood at first glance. The lettering is plain, the words are few in number, and the background is pleasing and serves to emphasize the lines of the drawing.

GENERAL CONSIDERATIONS

When the speaker is presenting his talk formally to an audience of 100 or more people and must condense into 20 minutes a paper that in published form would take 1 hour or more to read, it is most important that the slides be simple and easily comprehended. When the audience is smaller or the presentation time is longer, as in a seminar or colloquium where each member of the audience is definitely familiar with the speaker's field of work, slides may be more complex—especially when they are left on the screen for a long time—but they must still be legible and comprehensible.

A speaker may feel that he can pack more information into a limited period by the use of a large amount of visual material. But by so doing, he will not have time to explain the slides adequately, and may thus confuse his audience. On the other hand, if too few slides are used, the speaker may frequently leave on the screen a slide that has no relation to what he is talking about. This divides the attention of the audience between the speaker's words and the unrelated slide. The spectator may close his eyes and go to sleep at this point. To bridge the gap, a slide containing a photo illustrating something related to the subject being discussed may be used to retain the spectator's interest.

Turning lights on and off several times during a slide presentation should be avoided, if possible. This causes the speaker to lose the atention of the audience. If slides are not to be used during the whole time of the presentation, they should be grouped into one section of the talk, either the middle or the end.

To maintain smooth continuity of the talk with the slide presentation, the projectionist must change slides at the appropriate time. This is best done at technical conventions by providing the speaker with a push button or switch which actuates a light or buzzer signal at the projector to notify the projectionist when to change slides. If neither is available, an audible signal device, such as tapping the microphone, ringing a bell, or some such signal, is preferable to the speaker requesting *next slide please*. If the projectionist is provided with a marked copy of the script denoting the slide changes, smooth continuity is obtained. This procedure, of course, requires the speaker to adhere closely to the script in order to avoid confusing the projectionist.

USE OF COLOR

Color transparencies of equipment or operations are readily obtained nowadays by amateur or professional photographers. Charts, graphs, or even tables are improved by the judicious use of color. Such slides are readily produced by making a negative of a black and white drawing, chart, graph, or table. Hand coloring may be used for the white areas to improve the general eye appeal and to achieve greater clarity. This hand coloring is easily done by use of water colors or, better yet, dyes. A brush or cotton swab on a toothpick or *Q-tips* obtained at any drug store may be used for application. The more important portions of a curve or graph can be emphasized by applying brighter colors than on the less important areas. Such slides are attractive and comparatively inexpensive. Good taste will dictate the necessity of avoiding gaudiness in the use of the color dyes; a general color harmony throughout a slides series should prevail.

If a commercial artist is available, or if the speaker has artistic talent himself, the slide copy may be prepared by the use of dull-finished colored papers, such as *color-aid paper* available in a wide variety of colors. Contrasting lines may be placed on this paper by the use of narrow, adhesive tapes. Shadowed or cross-hatched areas can be produced, and the art work photographed in color. Such slides are expensive, unless the speaker can do the work himself. An airbrush can be used with advantage for shading and creating three-dimensional effects. By the use of polaroid materials and a rotating polarizer on the projector, animated effects may be obtained to indicate flow or other motion. This is usually quite expensive, however. Other advanced techniques include wide-screen projection and the use of two or even three projectors to achieve unusual effects. A common practice with two projectors is to use a solid-color gelatin mounted as a slide in one of the projectors and a negative slide in the other. This can give the effect of white letters on a colored background, which is very attractive and more pleasing than a black background. By the use of two projectors, several different overlays may be projected over one main illustration.

PLAN AHEAD

Slides can be expensive, if the services of artists and professional photographers are utilized to meet close deadlines. On the other hand, if the technical speaker plans ahead and uses his own ingenuity, he may produce slides that stand out and rouse the admiration of his fellow scientists and engineers.

Why not try to make your slide presentation just a bit different—just a bit better? Perhaps your paper may win a medal, or at least you will be complimented for your efforts.

Source of Material

1   *Engineering and Scientific Charts for Lantern Slides*, sponsored and published by the American Society for Mechanical Engineers, New York, *ASA Bulletin*, Z15, 1-1932, reaffirmed 1947, reprinted 1950.

2 Slide memoranda—Los Angeles Section, Institute of the Aeronautical Sciences, 7660 Beverly Blvd., Los Angeles.
3 B. A. Jones: *Make Slides Worthwhile*, preprint of paper presented before Society of Automotive Engineers, Detroit, Michigan, January 1952.
4 B. A. Jones: *Slides: Confusing or Clear*, Supt. of Services, Information Div., Research and Engineering Dept., Ethyl Corp., Detroit, Michigan. Reprint of paper presented before the Division of Chemical Literature, American Chemical Society—second printing, July 1955.
5 Eastman Kodak Publication No. S-8, *Photographic Production of Slides and Filmstrips*, 1955.
6 L. E. Owen: *The Illustration of Technical Talks—Lantern Slides*, Goodyear Atomic Corp., Portsmouth, Ohio, September 12, 1961.

Discussion and problems

1 Why are "the graphs or slides published in technical papers . . . rarely suitable for use in slides"?
2 What is "the prime motive of the slide"?
3 Summarize the eight rules for preparing good slides. Can you explain the why's and wherefore's of the rules? How do these rules correspond with the advice offered in the previous article, "Lantern Slides and Such: How to Cope with Data and Slides"?
4 What is a common fault of presenting tables in slide form? Why are "curves or bar diagrams preferable to tables for presenting data in slide form"?
5 When should data points be plotted on curves for slide presentation?
6 How many simple equations should be shown on a slide? How can a speaker present complicated mathematical derivations?
7 Summarize the author's advice on preparing a flow diagram for slide presentation.
8 When can complex slides be used?
9 What is the danger of using too many slides in a given period of time? of using too few slides?
10 Why is it often convenient to group slides into one section of a talk? What are the recommended ways for a speaker to signal the projectionist to change slides?

11 Following Romig's advice on preparing and using slides, design appropriate tables, graphs, mathematical formulae, and flow diagrams for slide presentation in a twenty-minute technical talk on an industrial process, e.g., the manufacture of iron or the refining of crude oil. Be sure to prepare slides that fit the purpose of your talk and that "make it easier for the hearer to follow, comprehend, and retain" the main ideas that you are trying to put across. Carefully plan the use of each slide: when and how long it will be used, and what you plan to say about it. Prepare a written outline of your entire talk, including the necessary details about the slides.

12 What are some of the advantages of using color slides? Relying on the advice of Romig and your own skills, prepare some color slides for the technical talk assigned in Question 11 above. Do you think that your color slides are more effective than similar ones in black and white?

Helping an audience to "see" slides *

Edwin W. Still's *article was written while he was a communication specialist in the Light Military Electronics Department, General Electric Company. In the excerpt reprinted below he emphasizes the importance of helping listeners to understand slides. The technical speaker must make sure that he is not analyzing data in slides while his listeners are still reading printed information on the slides or groping for an idea of what the slides are intended to show. The author suggests ways to avoid this difficulty, as well as recommending how and when to show slides.*

THE IMPORTANCE OF PROPER ORIENTATION

A map and a speech are two very different things. The map is all there before you, every bit of it, all at the same time. You can pick and choose and look at the part that interests you. You can make up your own logical order of reading to satisfy your own particular interests or needs.

Not so with a speech. The speaker must establish the logical order with proper orientation and movement from basic reference points to finer detail. If he jumps immediately into talking about Hector and Bird Island, you usually don't have much chance to stop him and ask him where they are. In reading the map, of course, you could glance up or down to the title or over-all outline of the map to get the orientation

---

* Excerpted from Edwin W. Still, "Can They *See* What You *Say* When You Speak?" *IRE Transactions on Engineering Writing and Speech*, EWS-2 (January 1959), pp. 24-29. Originally presented at Second National Symposium IRE-PGEWS. Reprinted by permission of IEEE and the author.

you suddenly found that you need. A speech then, should be heard, not like a map, but like a map is read.

This difference between a map and the reading of it illustrates the point that visual aids must aid, not hinder, your speech.

We sometimes seem to forget that a slide or a chart is not necessarily an aid just because it is visual. Whether it aids or hinders your speech will depend very much upon the way you use it.

If you want it to be an aid, don't expect your audience to read it in detail and listen to you at the same time. This is a difficult trick, even for those who can do it. Most of us, however, find ourselves put under considerable strain and usually end up by not getting either form of communication very well.

As the speaker who may have spent many hours in preparing the information displayed on the slide, you are more than familiar with it, and in a quick glance can probably spot the particular point that interests you and understand its meaning. Not so with the audience. They have to stop and read the whole thing, or at least enough of it for a good orientation before they can get the point which seems so obvious to you. In the meantime you have gone on developing it, and they have lost the meaning of your remarks.

THREE SOLUTIONS

What, then, to do? There are three possibilities.

In the first place, if you must use a detailed graph (Figure 1.), which might be good for a report or inclusion in a book but is not too appropriate for a speech, don't expect your audience to be able to understand it while you go on

212 EFFECTIVE SPEAKING FOR THE TECHNICAL MAN

talking to them on the basis of information which is contained in the graph. Give them a chance to read it first.

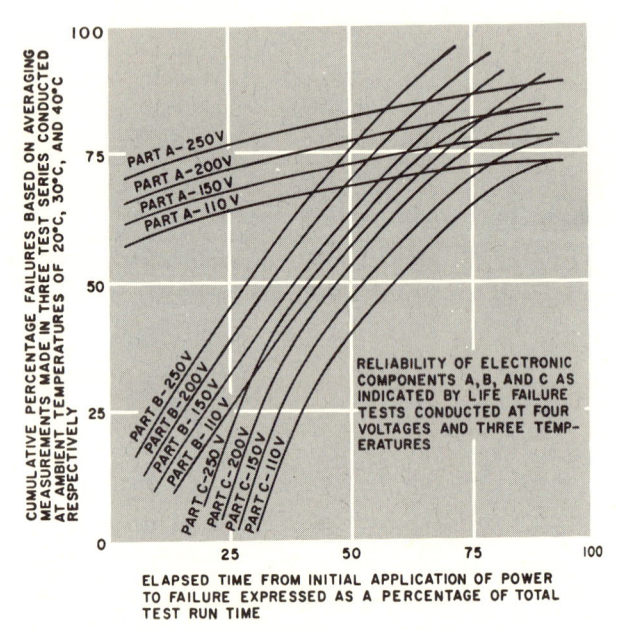

Figure 1.

In other words, just stop talking and let them read. (To the speaker: Wait in silence while you read silently to yourself the following which is what the audience is reading from the slide. Reliability of Electronic Components A, B, and C as indicated by life-failure tests conducted at four voltages and three temperatures. Cumulative percentage failures based on averaging measurements made in three tests series conducted at ambient temperatures of 20°C., 30°C., and 40°C. respectively. Elapsed time from initial application of power to failure expressed as percentage of total test run time.)

Now that they have had a chance to read the title and the information which is given along both the horizontal and vertical axes (the abscissa and the ordinate), the speaker could more safely go on to talk to the audience about the particular curve or set of curves.

Suppose, however, that as the speaker you just don't like silence. Or, more reasonably, that you are afraid the audience in reading the graph by itself will not orient itself as well as you might wish. The second possibility then, is to orient them yourself. This means that before you start talking about any detailed part of the graph, you will orient them by first reading aloud the title, and then pointing out the information which you have placed along each axis, reading it aloud for them. Only after a directed orientation such

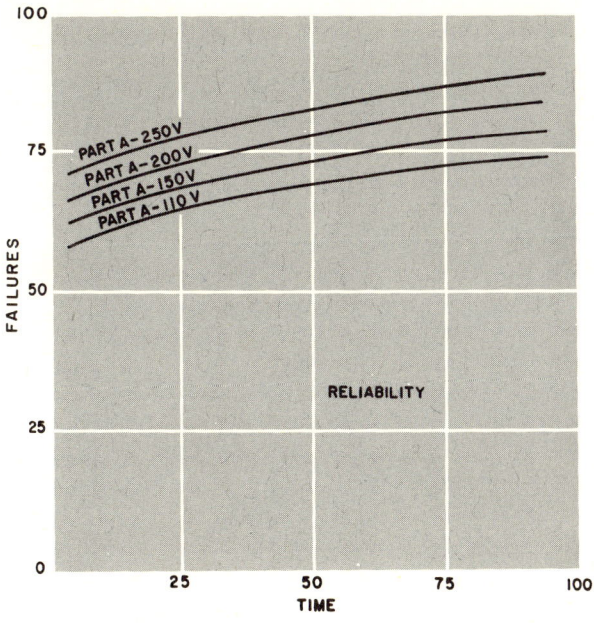

Figure 2.

as this can you safely proceed to discuss detail. Don't expect them to make their own orientation at the same time that you are discussing detail which depends upon an understanding of that orientation.

The third possibility, and really the best one, is not to use this graph at all. Save it for your report. Then prepare a set of graphs which cover the same information and are designed to be used with your speech.

If for example, you wanted to talk about Part A, you might prepare a graph as shown in Figure 2.

You will notice that the information in the title and along each axis has been cut to the very minimum. If you need any of the other detail which appeared on the original graph, you will give it to them in your speech as you talk to them about the graph. If it is not necessary, you will leave it out

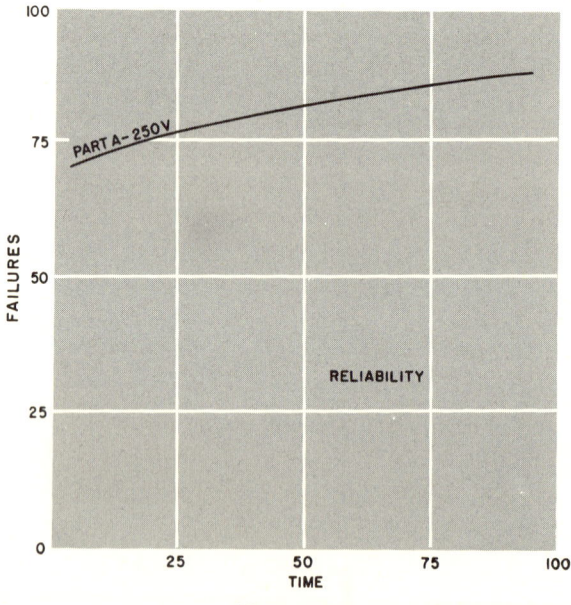

Figure 3.

and you will not have confused them. In addition, only the particular curve which interests you is shown, and the audience is not confused by the many others on the original graph.

If, of course, you are interested in showing the interrelationship of the curves, you might well start with a single curve (Figure 3), explain its meaning, and then go on in another slide like Figure 2 to show the family of curves of which it is a part.

If you wanted to show the inter-relationship of the three families of curves, you would then go on to a third slide (Figure 4) which would add the others.

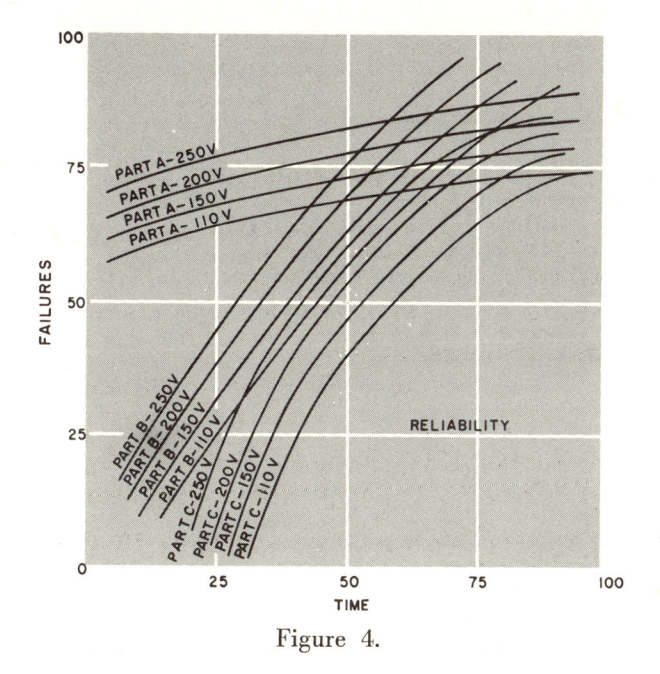

Figure 4.

Thus, the meaning of the three sets of curves could be made quite clear.

In summary, then, if you want your visual aid to aid and not hinder, don't expect your audience to read its detail while listening to you. Instead, choose one of three possible approaches: stop talking while they read, read it for them, or put on the slide only those things which it is essential for them to see.

BRIDGING SLIDES

Incidentally, before leaving this business of visual aids, you might want to note two minor and yet important things. When in the midst of our slides we wanted to talk for a while, we didn't blast your eyes by either turning on the house lights or subjecting you to the glare of a plain white screen. We used a softer green light to bridge the relatively short space between the two sets of slides.

In addition, the material of the speech has been planned so the periods which are completely audio come at the beginning and the end of the speech. This not only keeps all the slides together and thus minimizes the amount of adjustment the audience has to make from house lights to screen light and back to house lights again; but also puts the periods when the house lights are on at beginning and end. This is the most desirable time, for it is here that it is most valuable for the speaker to have the face-to-face contact with his audience. The period at the beginning enables you to get acquainted with him and him with you before he becomes simply a voice out of the darkness and you are so many indeterminate shapes. At the end you have the chance to check up again and see if he really looks as bad as he sounds. Or if you like what he said, to try to remember the person from whom you heard it.

Discussion and problems

1 Compare the orientation necessary for understanding a map to the proper orientation for understanding a slide.
2 Explain the three ways in which a speaker can properly introduce a slide before discussing particular details that interest him. Which way might insure simpler slide design? Can you think of other ways in which a speaker can properly introduce slides?
3 What general rules can you offer for introducing or orienting an audience to any visual aid?
4 What sort of lighting does the author suggest for bridging the gap between slides (when the speaker finds it necessary to talk for awhile)? Why does he recommend that a speaker use slides in the middle of a talk rather than at the beginning or end? How does Still's advice on bridging gaps between slides and on grouping slides in one section of a talk compare with the advice in the previous article, "Slides for Technical Talks"?
5 Formulate a general set of rules for the technical speaker who decides to use slides in a technical talk. The rules should cover the following areas: selecting the kind and amount of information to be placed on a slide; designing the form of a slide (tables vs. graphs, kinds of graphs, etc.); preparing slides (lettering, spacing, color, etc.); and using slides (proper orientation for an audience, grouping slides, bridging gaps between slides, lighting, changing slides, etc.). You may wish to refer to the last four articles covering slides and visual aids.

How to improve your talk with demonstrations *

Roger C. Wonson is a Senior Engineer in the Missile Systems Division of Raytheon Company at Bedford, Massachusetts. Like many engineers who are required to make technical presentations, he knows that a speaker often must demonstrate equipment and experiments. Closed-circuit projection TV and closed-circuit TV now enable large audiences to witness demonstrations such as the high-frequency operation of transistors. Using TV to demonstrate a piece of sophisticated equipment or a process to a large audience requires planning and suitable audiovisual facilities, but as the author points out, the effort can result in better understanding by the audience.

THE NEED FOR DEMONSTRATIONS

Demonstrations can improve the effectiveness of technical presentations. Experiments are often conducted in the laboratory in support of reviews or "new-to-the-art" presentations, and these experiments provide a source of ready-made test sets which can be used as demonstration equipment. This article describes how to implement demonstrations using closed circuit television, and suggests possible arrangements for effective presentation. Several examples illustrate the techniques.

---

* Reprinted from Roger C. Wonson, "How to Improve Your Talk With Demonstrations," *The Electronic Industries*, A Chilton Publications (October 1960), pp. 218-220, 222, 224. Reprinted by permission of the publisher and author.

ARRANGING CCTV FACILITIES

Figure 1 shows the layout for closed-circuit projection TV. The demonstrations are located backstage and are lined-up in order of their appearance. For the picture from the TV projector to be satisfactory, the auditorium and stage must be in subdued light so the screen must be shielded from

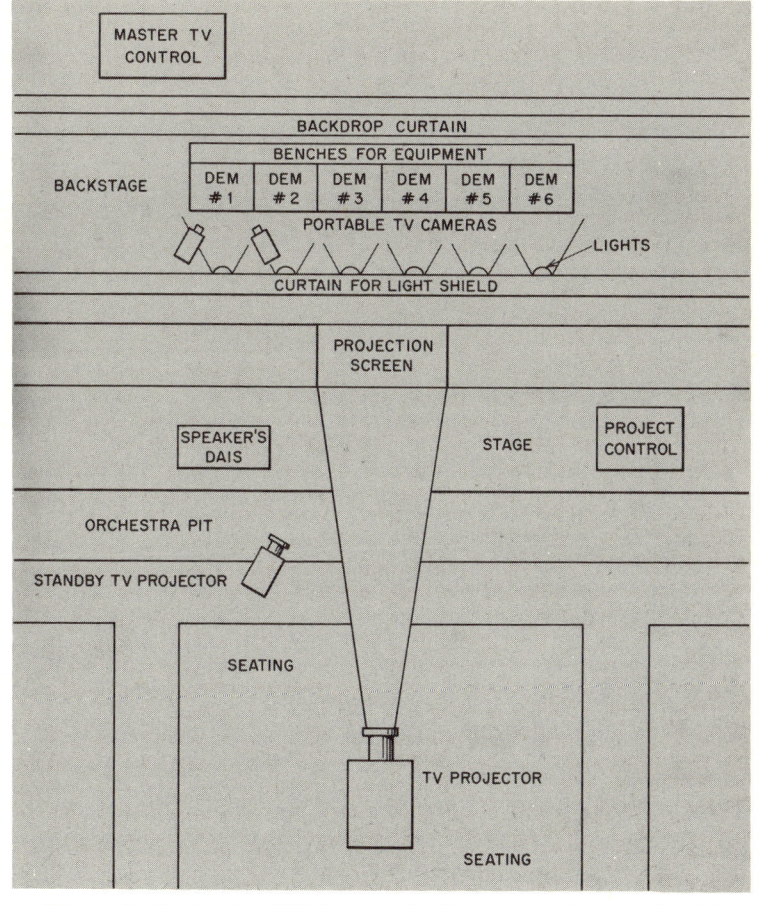

Figure 1. Projection TV layout. Auditorium and stage should be in subdued light.

lights from the demonstration area. To give the appearance of a "live presentation," the screen and curtains can be raised both before and after the talk and also during the intermission. The oral presentation should be planned to allow time for adjusting the cameras and for adjusting the working demonstrations. During this time interval the audience can be prepared for the next demonstration, for example by showing a schematic diagram of the next step with one of the cameras or with a slide projector. Two cameras

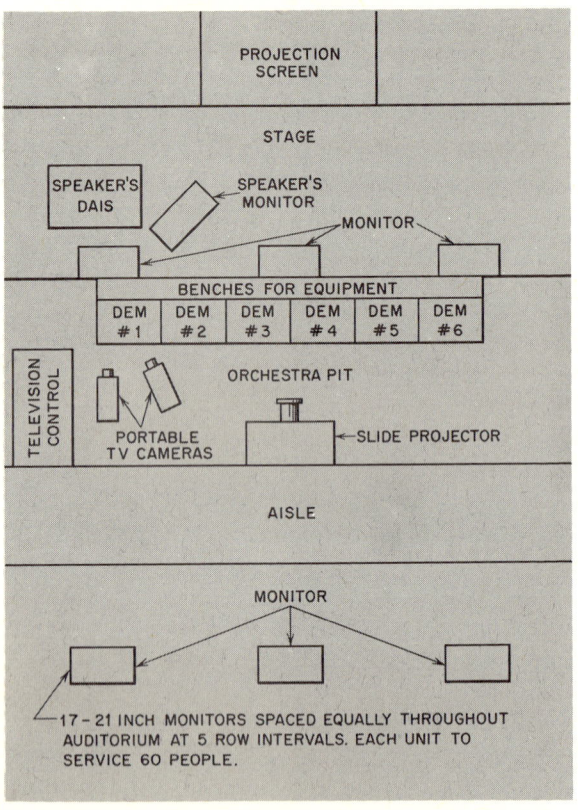

Figure 2. Using monitors. Demonstrations should be large to show fine detail.

can be very useful. For example, if one wanted to display the bias conditions and their effect on the circuit, one camera could be showing the bias source with the other camera showing the circuit output and its effect by varying this bias. A loud speaker can be installed for communications between the backstage demonstration crew and the lecturer.

USING MONITORS

Figure 2 shows an alternate arrangement for using CCTV. Here, monitors interspersed throughout the audience are used instead of projected television. The monitors in this particular presentation are twenty-inch diameter kinescopes. In this case, the demonstrations should be large enough so that people seated furthest from the monitors can read the fine detail. This, of course, is no problem with projection TV because of the very large size of the screen. With individual monitors the auditorium need not be darkened as much as when projection TV is used; therefore, the demonstrations can be set-up in the orchestra pit or in front of the stage. The same arrangement is used here as is used with projection TV—the demonstrations are lined up so that the camera can be moved from left to right in order of the demonstration appearance.

TIPS FOR THE SPEAKER

Obviously the speaker and the people working the demonstration equipment backstage should be thoroughly familiar with the presentation. The speaker can help the camera crew by informally telling them—during the demonstration— what he wants them to do, and the person on the demonstration equipment can also help the camera crew by pointing to the demonstration under discussion. Wherever possible, one or two trial runs should be made to smooth out the presentation.

APPARATUS

Typical TV projection apparatus is shown in Figure 3. With this particular apparatus, the projected picture size is approximately 16 x 16 feet. Fine detail such as numbers and figures on an ordinary 5 in. oscilloscope graticule can easily be seen on this screen. Figure 4 shows the backstage demonstrations and camera equipment. Note that meters and oscilloscopes which are integral parts of normal test apparatus are used. This will be further discussed.

Figure 3. Typical projection TV screen set-up. Screen is 16x16 feet.

IDEAS FOR INSTRUMENTATION

The demonstration ideas outlined here are for a technical presentation of the high-frequency operation of transistors, but the ideas will help in setting up demonstrations for any type of technical demonstration. For example: Figure 5 is a demonstration of apparatus which uses a mechanical sweep-drive connected to a power supply to vary its output. This variable voltage output is applied to the circuit to be demonstrated. Both cause and effect can be displayed on an oscilloscope and meters. These are simultaneously projected on the screen. The mechanical sweep-drive could also be connected to generators or other pieces of test equipment for advantageously showing a particular phenomenon or overall effect. Figure 6 shows an oscilloscopic form of presentation. Here the oscilloscope graticule is made from a piece of plexiglass.

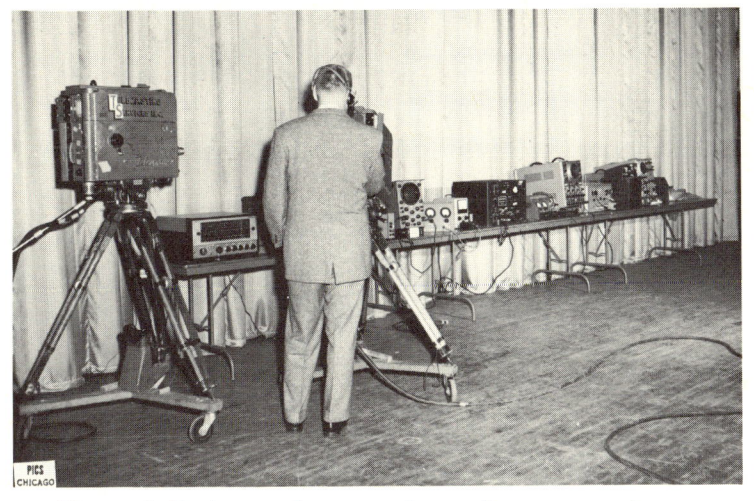

Figure 4. Backstage demonstration and camera equipment.

Figure 5. Demonstration using a mechanical sweep-drive.

The information is scribed upon the surface of the plexiglass to show the information necessary for the demonstration. Also, meters can be changed or marked to fit the needs of the demonstration.

A TEST CIRCUIT

One idea for displaying the performance of a test circuit is shown in Figure 7. The main purpose of the display is to show the effects of internal feedback in the transistor under test. This is done by disconnecting the neutralization circuit switch S-1. The swept input and output response is indicated on the dual beam oscilloscope. Without neutralization the ambiguity in the input will be noticeable. The neutralization can be connected and the external neutralizing circuit adjusted for complete cancellation of the internal feedback in the transistor; then the circuit will be neutralized. This whole operation can be performed in front of the TV camera. Bias supply voltages and currents to this circuit can also be varied and the result observed on the dual beam oscilloscope. The

Figure 6. Oscilloscope presentation uses a special graticule.

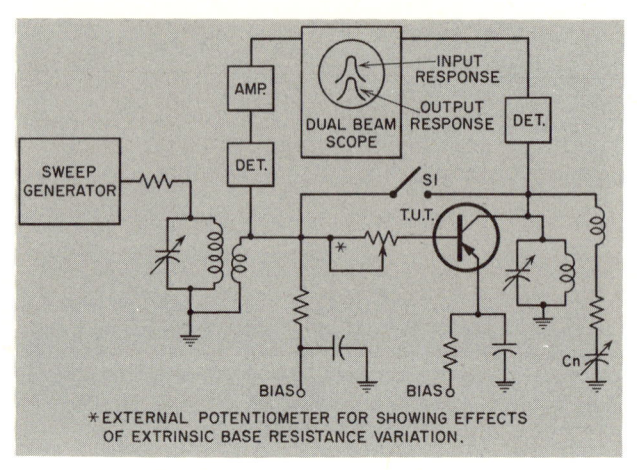

Figure 7. Typical operating display circuit.

ambient temperature of the transistor, or the circuit, can be raised or lowered and the effects displayed. A VTVM can of course be substituted for the oscilloscope showing output voltage level change, but the oscilloscope can show this as well as the change in frequency and band width which the

Figure 8. Author demonstrates transistorized FM transmitter. Transmitter—encased in plastic—was later shown over CCTV.

VTVM cannot show. This test circuit arrangement may be an isolated case, but it does exemplify a typical demonstration under actual operating conditions.

DEMONSTRATING OSCILLATOR EFFICIENCY

Figure 8 shows an FM transmitter operated by a single transistor. This transmitter was constructed in the laboratory as a practical application for measuring oscillator efficiency and mounted in a clear plastic case. Since the internal parts can be seen, it is a good demonstration not only for the test previously mentioned but also for referencing a number of points during the lecture. The output of the FM transmitter is detected by a communications receiver connected to the house sound system. After a few introductory remarks during which time the FM transmitter is employed, it is taken back stage and put on top of the receiver for size comparison to be seen over the television system. The camera is then moved in for a close view of the transistorized transmitter so that the internal parts can be seen by the audience. The circuit diagram is shown in Figure 9.

CONCLUSIONS

The engineer should consider implementing his talk with any and all of the test sets that he has used in experimentation since the test equipment can help to emphasize the points of discussion. Standard laboratory test circuitry can and should be used. Using oscilloscopes, mechanical sweep-drives, oscillographs, digital read out voltmeters, and in other ways increasing the effectiveness of the demonstration, results in better understanding by the audience. Furthermore, the demonstration may prove to be extremely valuable to the

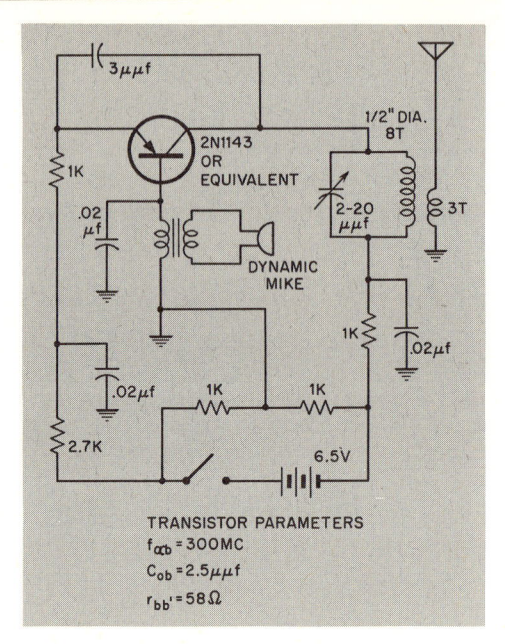

Figure 9. FM transmitter circuit.

laboratory. This type of presentation is not always practical for short (20-minute-type) technical discussions, but can be very effective for longer (2-hour) lectures.

Discussion and problems

1 When are demonstrations of equipment, processes, or experiments helpful or even necessary in a technical talk? Give examples. What technical demonstrations have you seen that were particularly effective?
2 What speaking and audiovisual rules do you think should govern the planning and use of demonstrations in a technical talk (introducing and explaining the demonstration, arranging and designing it for easy comprehension, amount of practice required, etc.)?
3 What sort of technical demonstrations can best be shown on closed-circut television, whether for large or small audiences?

What technical demonstrations have you seen on a projection screen or a monitor that actually were more effective because TV was used?

4 Give a 20-minute technical talk in which you use a demonstration to help explain one of the following: (1) how a piece of equipment is designed, (2) how an apparatus functions, or (3) how a process or procedure is carried out. Make sure that your technical talk emphasizes speaking as well as showing. Practice your demonstration, and prepare a written outline of your entire talk, including detailed plans for showing and explaining the mechanism or apparatus.

5 If possible, use closed-circuit television to give a 20-minute technical talk to your class. You may want to use a demonstration as part of your talk if you have had previous TV experience. Ask the class to comment on your performance (after playing back the video tape, you may be your own best critic). What advice can you offer a technical speaker who speaks in front of a television camera?

Microphone technique *

Paul Taylor *is news director of radio station WNPV, Lansdale, Pennsylvania. His wide experience in radio and television is reflected in his emphasis on the various speech skills necessary for mastering effective microphone technique. Because the individual characteristics of a microphone can inflence how a speaker sounds, the author also explains the characteristics of three types of microphones commonly used.*

GOOD SPEECH TECHNIQUE

One of the greatest frauds being perpetrated on an innocent and eager portion of the population is a course taught in virtually every dramatic and broadcasting school in the country—Microphone Technique. A scientific-sounding flow of indistinct language, masquerading as genuine instruction, is put to the student. Fortunately, most students don't absorb the instruction, and thus, are saved any intensification of their lack of knowledge of the subject.

What these charlatans should be teaching is speech technique—more exactly phonetics, which is a fairly exact procedure, and singing, which isn't. However, it would be dishonest and unfair of me to suggest that nothing need be known of the microphone, if you are obliged to speak into one to earn money, or some other nefarious purpose. The

---

* From Paul Taylor, "Microphone Technique," *IRE Transactions on Engineering Writing and Speech*, EWS-2 (January 1959), pp. 30-32. Originally presented at Second National Symposium IRE-PGEWS. Reprinted by permission of IEEE and the author.

course should be called Microphone Characteristics. For it is the individual character of the microphone plus your skill in speech that control how you will sound, and how effective you will be. There is no special way of speaking to a microphone—a way mysteriously different from the way one speaks normally—that will produce an effective performance.

By talking about the nature of the microphone, and not special "techniques," the course could be cut to one week instead of ten or more, and with bright pupils, to about ten minutes. The microphone, contrary to the belief of many, will not correct faults of speech. And you know that the microphone is the most objective, impersonal, and unsentimental ear in the world. It repeats exactly what it hears.

Therefore, good microphone technique must be based on good speech technique, or all the time is wasted.

Therefore, what is good speech, and what is its purpose?

In my view, good speech has three main functions: to be clearly understood, to move the hearer, and to produce beauty.

COMPONENTS OF GOOD SPEECH

The mechanics of good speech, in my experience, consist of the following components. They all exist individually, and can be analyzed in that way. All blend imperceptibly with each other to produce good speech.

These elements are: freedom of vocal production, freedom of articulation, free enunciation, good rhythm, good intonation, and good pronunciation.

Freedom of vocal production means no hindrances or muscular inhibitions of the vocal muscles. The vocal cords must be drawn tight, close together. Their tension must exactly match the pressures provided by the breathing muscles that supply air for the sound. But the tension must be directed along the proper axes, and in proper balance with each other. When the tensions go awry, you have voice trouble. But relaxation is not the answer: with relaxation, you have no sound. A good vocal sound consists of ease, brightness, fullness, range, flexibility, and stamina.

ARTICULATION

Freedom of articulation means that the tongue, lips and teeth—the speech factory—function without tension, with accuracy, and flexibility, and do so with the scope of movement dictated by the demands of the moment.

Good enunciation means the proper—and consistent—formation of the vowels and consonants that constitute language.

RHYTHM

Good rhythm means a constant change, according to the meaning, in the rhythmic structure of phrases, and clauses. Constantly varying thesis and arsis throw American speech into balance. The absence of rhythm, even in prose, robs vitality, makes meaning difficult of apprehension, and produces monotony and boredom.

Good intonation is rhythm translated to pitch, the rise and fall of the voice in the patterns of the language, and within that, in the individual, the whole colored by the meaning and the mood.

Good pronunciation is the easiest to acquire, and the easiest to change. Even a speaker with a marked local accent, or a national one, can have good pronunciation.

It is not necessary to form consonant sounds with the energy of a construction blast to have them be accurate, or to carry as far as is needed. A light, but accurate formation is enough, and it is easier on the listeners' ears. Consistency of vowel formation is of great importance. The A in arch, father, and the diphthong portion of the "ou" in house should all have the same sound. In almost everyone's speech, basic vowel sounds go through strange mutations as they occur in various words.

If inconsistencies of enunciation are coupled with equal inconsistencies of articulation, and all of those incompletely done, the result is bound to be vagaries of speech that are hard to understand, even if not filtered through the particular hostilities of the less expensive microphones.

Just as law cases are won in the office, with the court being merely the arena of proof, so good microphone technique is won in the human throat, with the mike being its arena of proof. In a word then, with good speech technique, microphone technique can be forgotten.

Almost.

MICROPHONE CHARACTERISTICS

At risk of offending the men who may perhaps have designed these microphones, let me briefly outline the basic, generalized characteristics of the three types of microphones most often found.

The ribbon is almost exclusively used in radio stations, and will turn up in public address systems only when the proceedings are being broadcast. The ribbon is generally a high quality microphone, with a smooth responsive curve, and considerable sensitivity. It tends to give a "soft" reproduction. It has a tendency to accent the bass frequencies. It will accent bass particularly when the sound source is very close, and if too close and at too high a level, the ribbon will paralyze, producing distortion and a drop off in high-frequency response.

Therefore, a voice that is "bassy" should operate at a safe distance, from 8 inches to a foot. If such a voice must work close to the mike, the energy level should be reduced, and the wave front directed at an angle across the face.

The dynamic microphone turns up most of the time in P.A. systems. And usually it is an inexpensive one, with a curve, but not necessarily a good one. At close range it is particularly susceptible to "popping" of plosive consonants, which include t, d, g, and k, as well as the obvious b and p. Overloaded at too close range, it will add a metallic ring, distort highs, and hiss sibilants like an asp. It is less inclined to distort bass at close range or to paralyze, but it can be done. The best distance again is from 8 inches to a foot for the average voice. A higher pitched voice should work somewhat closer, and at a drop in energy level. Also at close range, any voice should be used across the face of it, at angles from 45 to 0 degrees. The chief reason for this angle is to avoid the popping.

Crystal and ceramic microphones turn up with an alarming frequency in P.A. systems. They are getting better all the time, thanks to the efforts of you gentlemen, but they are not yet good, by stereophonics standards. At a distance of 6 inches to a foot, depending on the voice, they give a good response. Up close they can be popped, and will distort highs somewhat like a hungry kitten. They will not as a rule distort bass. And they can be addressed head on with minimum disaster.

These then, assuming that the experience of my ear coincides with laboratory statistics, are the general characteristics of microphones likely to be encountered in public address systems. They generally come in three grades of excellence: adequately acceptable, acceptable, and lousy.

ADJUSTING TO THE MICROPHONE

Without a recapitulation then, the type of voice, high, low, soft, breathy, or sharp, should adjust his approach to the microphone, according to what type of microphone it is. And the microphone should be definitely remembered. There is nothing more annoying than the speaker who swivels his head about from side to side, in order to include all his audience in his gaze. But he fails to include all of it within sound range. Off the microphone beam you must read lips, and when he passes the face of it, you must hold your ears. If it becomes necessary to turn the head, do so in a way that will include the live end of the mike always in the direct line of the speech propagator. Equally annoying is the speaker with the soft, sometimes inaudible voice, who will not go near the microphone. This requires the operator to open the gain to heroic levels, with the result that feedback shatters the room. Strangely, such speakers seem to have built-in wave cancellation at the feedback frequencies. As Hamlet says, "Pray avoid it altogether."

EMPIRICAL TECHNIQUES

The following advice is so primitive that it will undoubtedly offend the finely trained discriminations of the scientific mind. But when you can't read the labels, and you don't know from experience, the best empirical way to determine whether the microphone has any value is its appearance. Generally, a microphone that has a well-made look on the outside will probably have a well-made inside. With reservations. And the best empirical way to determine how best to use a given microphone in a P.A. system is to listen to it. If possible use the mike for a few minutes before the audience arrives. Experiment with distances, angle, and your own voice quality and volume level. When it sounds best, that is the position and delivery that ought to be used.

FURTHER SUGGESTIONS

A few exotic suggestions now for those who might care to pursue the effective speaking into microphones a bit further. Get a good singing teacher, and a good phonetics teacher. A good phonetics teacher is not too rare a bird. A good singing teacher these days is hard to find. The phonetics teacher can develop the science if that word can be extended, of speech. The singing teacher will develop the power, range, flexibility, richness and endurance of the voice, *if* he is a good teacher. Finding a good singing teacher, unfortunately, is harder than finding an honest politician in the finest sense of that word. The only guide is to judge first the teacher as a person, and second by his or her effect on your vocal apparatus. If after a month or so of study your voice feels freer, sounds pleasanter, has greater range and expressivity and endurance, you have a good one, and should study for a year or two. If you find yourself getting hoarse, feeling uncomfortable muscle tensions in the throat, and not adding general range, get rid of him, fast. The Lord gave you one voice, and if it is ruined, it is almost impossible to redeem it.

Singing is recommended not to make a singer of you, unless you find your desire that. It is recommended as the best method in my experience to develop the voice per se. It is extremely difficult to teach sheer voice production, using speech only. One is not thoroughly conscious of tone, does not make the necessary demands, and tends to produce sound in the old speech ways when speech approaches alone are used.

CONCLUSIONS

I am aware that I have failed to give a few magic "do it yourself" words that will open up the whole wonderful world of microphone technique to the tyro. But the reason is that there aren't any. And I could not in honesty pretend that there were, just for the fleeting joy of posing as an expert.

I have tried instead to trace the origin of good microphone techniques—the basic speech ability of the individual. I have tried to show how the individual's ability can be blended to the demands of microphones of various sorts. And I have tried to show how best to overcome some of the pitfalls of using microphones if there is neither time or opportunity to approach speech in an exhaustive way. And I can only hope that success has attended my efforts.

There is one final basic ingredient essential to producing an over-all effective microphone presence: you have to care.

Discussion and problems

1 Why does Taylor believe that "there is no special way of speaking to a microphone . . . that will produce an effective performance"? What determines how well a speaker will sound using a microphone?
2 What is the basis of "good microphone technique"?
3 Explain the six components in the mechanics of good speech. What are the qualities of "good vocal sound"?
4 Summarize the general characteristics of three types of microphones discussed by the author. If you have had experience speaking before microphones, add your own observations.

5 What are some of the annoying habits of speakers who have not adjusted their speaking habits to the type of microphone used?
6 What is "the best empirical way to determine whether the microphone has any value"? Explain "the best empirical way to determine how best to use a given microphone in a P.A. system"?
7 What can a speaker learn about speaking from lessons in singing?
8 Practice speaking with various types of microphones, and discuss the microphone characteristics that you experienced.
9 Plan to give one of your technical speeches using a microphone and a P.A. system in a lecture hall or an auditorium (if your classmates cannot be present, use a tape recorder to record your speech). What did you learn from your experience that you can pass on to technical speakers using a microphone for the first time? Do you agree with the author that effective microphone technique depends on "the individual character of the microphone plus your skill in speech"?

Increasing information exchange at informal meetings *

Dr. E. W. Grieshaber is Published Products Manager, Visual Products Division, Minnesota Mining and Manufacturing Company. He was the leader of a group of 3M scientists who in 1960 introduced a new visual communication system employing a dry process copying machine and an overhead projector. Transparencies and an overhead projector can be used in administrative meetings to show agendas, charts, schedules, etc., as well as in technical groups to show data, drawings, and figures. In the following article, the author carefully explains the advantages of using an overhead projector to "increase information exchange."

IMPROVING VERBAL COMMUNICATION

If more people knew how inefficient verbal communication is, they would have far more apprehension about their effectiveness in speaking to a group. They'd feel it was largely a waste of time! What's more, the meeting at which no record is kept would be outlawed by management!

Yet, we all go to meetings where we have a constant struggle to keep our attention on what the speaker is saying. Then, when the meeting is over we come away with nothing except our own and our colleagues' powers of recall to remind us of decisions or assignments that might have been made.

---

* Reprinted from E. W. Grieshaber, "Increasing Information Exchange at Informal Meetings," *Research/Development Magazine* (March 1965), pp. 28-30, by permission of the publisher and author. Copyright 1967 by F. D. Thompson Publications, Inc.

Why, when so much progress has been recorded in electronic communication, has so little been done about improving our communicating when we're face to face. Are we satisfied we can't improve on the way this has been done since the time of Socrates? Or is it that most people are unaware of the fact that an alternative exists . . . that one can very easily make meetings more efficient . . . that verbal communication can be greatly improved.

A VISUAL COMMUNICATION SYSTEM

I'm going to describe a Visual Communication System which we use at 3M Company, a system which is rapidly growing in popularity at many schools, military establishments, and companies throughout the country. The system in any of its forms remains a simple but always effective means of information exchange. Essentially it is a form of attention control. It relies on showing information and discussing it at the *same time*. It takes cognizance of the results of studies (made by the Socony Mobile Oil Co. some years ago) which indicate that 83 percent of what we learn is through sight, and only 11 percent through sound. Further, in the case of general information, what we recall at a later period is on the average 20 percent of what we hear, 30 percent of what we see, but 50 percent of what we see and hear.

The tools that you need to upgrade your meeting results are:

    1. an overhead projector
    2. a transparency or copy maker
    3. film and paper

Since these items are readily available from a variety of sources, I'll not dwell on them other than to state that the

Overhead Projector was specifically designed to be different from and to have a number of very real advantages over any other type of projector. It was designed for meetings!

The speaker operates the projector from the front of the group; he faces the group in a fully lighted room. Eye contact—that precious catalyst to effective communication—is never lost.

The projector uses transparencies which lie face up on the large stage where they can be easily read. You can point to parts of the material or write with a grease pencil to develop information for extra emphasis. By turning the machine on, you can draw all eyes to the screen—then back to you again by turning it off. In short you can control attention and the rate at which you transmit information.

SOME EVERYDAY RULES

Now, let's consider some everyday uses you can make of this Visual Communication System. The first thing you'll notice in using the system is that you will organize more for desired results, and you will save time. You can start your meeting by projecting a copy of your agenda on the screen. In fact, having it on the screen early so your people see it as they enter the room creates an atmosphere of organization and direction. You'll get under way more easily.

You made the transparency from a penciled original on paper. Now give this original to a meeting secretary—a competent, active member of the group. Have him note very briefly under your headings the substance of the decisions made as the meeting progresses. Now leave him alone; we'll get back to him before this meeting breaks up.

You have some cost information to present. You've worked hard over it and have simplified it to its essentials. While the conclusion or the last line of your chart is important, you want consideration of each item there without the skipping and jumping ahead which your audience is so prone to do.

How do you accomplish this? Easiest thing in the world! You make a transparency of the chart you made up or had your secretary type out large and clear. Then you cover with plain paper the information you don't want your audience to see yet. By revealing the data line by line you focus attention where you want it. This technique is called, appropriately enough, revelation. And its effectiveness can't be beaten.

All right, you have a schedule to review and discuss. It involves laboratory, engineering, production, accounting, sales, and advertising people. They all speak a different language and feel their part in the program to be most critical of all. Here you can employ the overlay technique to advantage.

Start by projecting a transparency of an appropriate calendar. Have the spokesman for each group in turn lay his compatible transparency over the calendar. Thus schedule details are assembled stepwise in organized fashion. The entire group sees and appreciates the relationships and meshing of effort necessary to completing the job on time. You will have people working through the common denominator of the visual, and greater understanding will result. Also you can encourage the sense of urgency so vital to meeting your schedule.

How many times have you wanted to take information from a drawing on a man's board but hesitated to delay his work by removing the drawing from his board? This need pose no problem at all. A transparency of any part of the drawing can be made easily. Then you can be sure everyone sees the details as you see them.

Incidentally, you can use such a transparency for prints via your shop blueprint machine. However, don't make the mistake of handing them out during the meeting or your audience will divide their attention between you and the prints.

We started this discussion on the assumption that you wanted your meetings to run at peak efficiency. If necessary you can also go to your microfilm aperture file for a specific drawing, make a print of it, and then a transparency for display. This means that should an unforeseen need develop during the meeting itself, you need not be frustrated by the inability to get at the information or to convert it into a useful form promptly. In other words you can keep your meeting going.

Sometimes engineers, accustomed as they are to reading blueprints, prefer a print with a dark background and a light line. This need be no problem. Rather than going through an intermediate, one can choose a negative acting film.

THREE RULES

No discussion on the use of the communication technique is complete without attention to three basic rules. They relate to room arrangement, print size, and print complexity. Let's consider these rules in that order.

Unfortunately, the word projector has been related in people's minds to darkened rooms, screen flat on the wall, and equipment in the rear of the room. The overhead projector designed for front-of-the-room operation requires less conventional arrangements. To insure visibility by all the occupants in the room, a screen mounted in the corner with projector in normal relationship to the plane of the screen permits the speaker excellent eye contact with his audience without the disadvantage of obscuring the image on the screen.

As a general rule of thumb, unless one has a large screen, one should not attempt to make a transparency of fine print material and expect the audience to be able to see it. If you have difficulty reading your transparency original at eight to ten feet, the people in the rear of the room will have difficulty seeing it on the screen.

Lastly, simplicity is a virtue in this type of communication. A transparency having approximately six lines of print and dealing with a minimum of ideas is far preferable to one crowded with extraneous detail. In other words, think through the original and eliminate unnecessary information.

ADDING INFORMATION

You will find this system lends itself extremely well to that type of meeting where information is developed. In many instances participants at a meeting can sketch out their idea or concept and review it to the group. And, as that idea stimulates still another, you may find you have developed a patentable device. The original sketches, or the transparencies with grease pencil or felt pen additions, may well serve as the legal record of invention. Also, you will find that the collection of these originals and transparencies do away with the necessity of photographing the marks left on a blackboard at the meeting's close.

Let us go back now to the meeting you called starting with the agenda on the screen and your appointed secretary making brief notes. Rather than closing the meeting with an "O.K., you all know what you have to do. See you next week," or some such comment, why not try this? Summarize. And summarize most specifically and clearly this way. Take the secretary's notes. Make a transparency of them. Your notes, you will find, relate closely to the agenda. When you project the transparency, you can review step by step through your agenda what decisions you made and who was responsible specifically for the action you all had agreed upon as necessary.

As a matter of fact, you now can take the secretary's notes and make copies as well as transparency, so every person assigned an area of responsibility can leave the meeting with a copy of the minutes. Additionally, you will all have had a chance to review the assignments in light of the total project needs.

BENEFITS

Thus, your meetings can be held in less time with greater understanding and with a maintaining of the momentum which is so necessary to the success of your program. Saving time and improving understanding are the intrinsic benefits of the visual communication system.

Discussion and problems

1 Why does the author believe that visual communication should be used to reinforce verbal communication?
2 Why does he believe that an overhead projector is the most effective projection device to use in meetings?
3 What are the advantages of the "revelation" and "overlay" techniques?
4 What rules apply to room arrangement, print size, and print complexity?

5   How can an overhead projector be helpful in a "meeting where information is developed"?
6   What are the overall benefits of the visual communication system described by the author?
7   Plan a committee meeting of a group of students in which a topic of current scientific interest is discussed, or plan a problem solving conference which makes recommendations about a problem of current technical or scientific interest. Use an overhead projector to help "increase information exchange." To help in planning the committee meeting or problem solving conference, you may want to refer to "How to Chair a Committee and a Technical Meeting" by E. J. Tangerman, reprinted on pp. 138-145; and to Appendix D (Checklist for Planning and Conducting a Committee Conference). Did you find that an overhead projector helped to "increase information exchange"? Did it help you function more effectively as a chairman? What rules can you formulate for using overhead projectors in meetings and conferences?

APPENDICES

APPENDIX A

Manuscript and extemporaneous delivery in communicating information *

Among technical speakers, the topic of manuscripts and extemporaneous delivery in communicating information is much discussed, as evidenced in several of the articles in Part Two (Preparing and Delivering the Message) of this book. The research study described below represents an attempt to measure the effectiveness of manuscript and extemporaneous delivery in presenting information to an audience of university students. Every technical speaker needs to ponder the results of this study. **Dr. Herbert W. Hildebrandt** *is Associate Professor of Speech, as well as Secretary of the University and Assistant to the President, University of Michigan.* **Dr. Walter W. Stevens** *is Associate Professor of English and Speech at Montana State University. Both authors have published articles and books on speech communication.*

PURPOSE

A common assumption in rhetoric and public address is that extemporaneous delivery is superior to the use of a manuscript in presenting information to an audience. The purpose of the present study is to examine this belief by

---

* From Herbert W. Hildebrandt and Walter W. Stevens, "Manuscript and Extemporaneous Delivery in Communicating Information," *Speech Monographs* (November 1963), pp. 369-372. Reprinted by permission of the Speech Association of America and the authors.

testing the hypothesis that the extemporaneous and the manuscript methods of delivery can result in the same amount of information gain in an audience. Two subhypotheses studied are (1) that speakers do not vary significantly in the amount of information gain which they produce and (2) that speakers are equally skillful in using both methods of delivery.

PROCEDURE

For purposes of the experiment, manuscript speaking was defined as that form of delivery in which the speaker follows the page without deviation and without interpolation. Extemporaneous delivery was defined as a presentation in which the speaker prepared an outline of significant points, rehearsed once privately, and spoke from the outline with the majority of words chosen at the actual moment of utterance.

The subjects were students in the basic public speaking course at The University of Michigan. Of the eighteen sections participating, one third was the control group, another third heard the extemporaneous speeches, and the other third heard the presentations from manuscript. Assignments to the three groups were at random, and the students did not know in advance either of the speakers, the speech topic, the method of delivery being used, or the day they were to hear the speech.

To avoid disturbing the normal routine of the classes, the experimental topic was allied to the course and was built around the American orator, Robert M. LaFollette. The message was the constant. The initial draft of the speech was composed by two speakers, revised by them after criticism by several other readers, limited to thirty minutes, and delivered to a group of teaching fellows in speech for final suggestions.

Both speakers were familiar with the message and had had extensive training and practice in both manuscript and extemporaneous delivery. The rationale behind their selection was that both would be proficient in each form of presentation. Their tasks were fourfold: (1) composing the speech, (2) practicing the speech, (3) presenting the speech in the experimental situations, and (4) preparing the single examination for all groups, both experimental and control.

The short introductions of the speakers in all instances were alike in order to minimize the influence of prestige. To avoid partial memorization, the extempore presentations preceded those from manuscript, and only one rehearsal was permitted. The extemporaneous speech was taped in order to make certain that all items covered in the written test were included. The longest and the shortest presentations varied by less than two minutes.

A sixty-item multiple choice examination on the topic of La Follette served as both pretest and post-test. The administration of the former was two days prior to the delivery of the speeches, and the post-test occurred immediately after the presentations. Reliability for half the test, as determined by a correlation of the scores of the odd and the even numbered items of a pre-test administration to a control group, was .81. The coefficient of reliability for the entire test, as estimated by the Spearman-Brown modified formula, was .89.

No attempt was made to match groups, but an analysis of variance indicated that there were no significant differences among the means of pretest scores (control, 26.89; extemporaneous, 27.05; manuscript, 26.69; F, .58). Hence, the randomly selected groups can be considered as satisfactorily equated prior to the application of the stimulus.

The members of the control group (N-115) were not exposed to a speech about La Follette. Speaker A spoke to two groups extemporaneously (N-46) and read the manuscript speech to two groups (N-40). Speaker B spoke extemporaneously to two groups (N-49) and read the manuscript speech to two groups (N-44). The reason for the seeming inconsistency of only four groups per speaker instead of six was that two sections were combined in both the extemporaneous and the manuscript groups. Group size as a factor was considered negligible.

RESULTS

The first step in testing the major hypothesis was to determine whether the post-test means showed significant differences among the three groups—those hearing the extemporaneous speeches, those hearing the presentations from manuscripts, and those serving as the control. An F of 182.9, obtained by a one-way analysis of variance, indicated that the differences among the post-test means were significant far beyond the one percent level. A further study, using both an F-test and a t-test, showed that the control group mean was significantly lower than were the other two post-test means; thus, the variations in the mean scores may be attributed at least in part to the experimental stimuli.[1]

The second step was to use a multiple analysis of variance to compare the extemporaneous and the manuscript groups on the basis of the differences between their respective pre-

---

[1] Wilfrid J. Dixon and Frank J. Massey, Jr., *Introduction to Statistical Analysis* (New York: McGraw-Hill Book Co., 1957), p. 123.

Table 1. Changes in Scores from Pretest to Post-Test in the Groups Hearing Manuscript and Extempore Presentations by Two Speakers

Mode of Delivery	Speaker	N	ΣX	ΣX^2	$\Sigma(X-\bar{X})^2$	$\bar{X}$
MS	A	40*	873	20,579	1525.8	21.82
MS	B	40	696	14,222	2111.6	17.40
Extemp.	A	40	863	19,739	1119.8	21.58
Extemp.	B	40	854	20,086	1853.1	21.35
Total		160	3286	74,626	7139.3	

*Listeners who failed to take either the pretest or the post-test were eliminated from the experiment. To simplify computations, zero to nine cases were discarded at random from these subgroups so that all would be equal in size.

test and post-test means. This procedure indicated that the group hearing the extempore speech and the one hearing the presentation from manuscript did not differ significantly in the amount which they learned (see Table 2).

The major hypothesis, that the extemporaneous and the manuscript methods of delivery can result in the same amount of information gain in an audience, therefore, is not rejected. In other words, with the speakers and the hearers employed in this study, extemporaneous delivery, as compared with manuscript delivery, did not result in a greater information gain.[2]

The first subhypothesis, that speakers do not vary significantly in the amount of information gain which they produce, is rejected (F = 5.10; df = 1; significant at the five percent level). Thus, even with two speakers who appeared to be equally well trained and well prepared, the one was superior to the other as a communicator of information.

---

[2] The F of .63 was obtained through the procedure applicable to a mixed model—in this instance a fixed level of extemporaneous and manuscript delivery but a random level of speakers. The fixed level was tested with the interaction. See Bernard Ostle, *Statistics in Research* (Ames, Iowa: Iowa State University Press, 1954), pp. 361-364. However, even if the method of delivery had been tested against the within-means-squares, the F of 3.23 would have fallen short of 3.90, which is the five percent level.

Table 2. Summary of the Results of an Analysis of Variance

Source	Sum of Squares	df	Mean Square	F
Method of delivery (rows)	136.9	1	136.9	.63
Speakers (columns)	216.2	1	216.2	5.10*
Interaction	176.4	1	176.4	4.16*
Within	6610.3	156	42.37	
Total	7139.8	159		

*Significant at the five per cent level.

The second subhypothesis, that speakers are equally skillful in using both methods of delivery, also is rejected at the five percent level. Not only does an inspection of the differences of the means from pretest to post-test (A, manuscript method, 21.82; A, extempore, 21.58; B, manuscript, 17.40; B, extempore, 21.35) strongly suggest that a speaker may be more skilled in one method of delivery than in another, but also the statistical analysis of the interaction between speaker and method of delivery indicates rejection (F = 4.16; df = 1; significant at the five percent level). Finally, an application of the t-test to the means resulting from hearing Speaker B (t = 2.48; df = 78; significant at the two percent level) indicates that he produced greater information gains with the extemporaneous than with the manuscript mode of delivery.

DISCUSSION AND CONCLUSIONS

A study employing only two speakers must be regarded as introductory to the study of a rhetorical issue and as only the first step toward arriving at results warranting generalization. The conclusion for the present data, however, seems clear: It is not the method of presentation *per se* which determines the effectiveness of a speech, as measured by the amount learned; instead, it is the ability of the individual speaker in using a particular method. As common sense perhaps should have suggested all along, the statement in textbooks that the extemporaneous method is superior to reading aloud should be revised to read *Some speakers are more effective extemporaneously than they are when using a manuscript, and some use both methods with equal effectiveness.* The present study was with experienced speakers, and how many beginners could do as well with a manuscript as with the extempore method is a topic for further investigation.

The present experiment shows that even persons well trained in both methods of presentation may not be equally efficient in both. The success that one has in communicating information may be dependent upon the speaker's own ability with a given method. One should know in which manner he is most effective in giving information and then employ that type of presentation.

Finally, the present experiment indicates that delivery is important in determining the amount of information which listeners retain. That a significant difference arose when the two speakers were presumably equally well trained seems even stronger evidence of the importance of delivery than would have been true if the comparison had dealt with abilities markedly different.

APPENDIX B

Selected and annotated bibliography of useful information for technical speakers

BOOKS AND PAMPHLETS

CARSON, HERBERT L. *Steps in Successful Speaking.* Princeton, New Jersey: D. Van Nostrand Company, Inc., 1967. [A detailed discussion, with plentiful examples, of ten steps in preparing a speech. Helpful for public speakers.]

CASEY, ROBERT S. *Oral Communication of Technical Information.* New York: Reinbold Publishing Corporation, 1958. [Organization of material, composing a speech for oral delivery, delivering formal and informal speeches, the use of audiovisual aids.]

Conference Leadership. AF Manual 50-8. Washington: Department of the Air Force, 1956. [Duties and traits of a conference leader, problem solving techniques, preparing and conducting a conference, evaluating a conference leader, duties of a conferee.]

CONNOLLY, JAMES. *Effective Technical Presentations.* St. Paul, Minnesota: 3M Business Press, 1968. [Straightforward and practical help for technical speakers: fundamental concepts in communication, the audience, the message, supporting the message, visual support material, the final presentation, the group presentation.]

DIETRICH, JOHN E., and KEITH BROOKS. *Practical Speaking for the Technical Man.* Englewood, N.J.: Prentice-Hall, Inc., 1958. [Applies the fundamentals of speech to technical speaking situations. Chapters end with summarizing formulas which can be applied in appropriate situations.]

Effective Lecture Slides. Kodak Sales Service Pamphlet No. S-22. Eastman Kodak Company, Rochester, New York. [Concrete advice on preparing 2x2-inch slides that can be easily seen and understood. Advice also applies to other projected visuals. Plentiful examples.]

HAEMER, K. W. *Making the Most of Charts: An ABC of Graphic Presentation.* Presented to the General Assembly of The 15th Technifax Seminar—Workshop in Visual Communication, Technifax Corporation, Holyoke, Massachusetts, April 23, 1959. Booklet copyright 1960, American Telephone and Telegraph Company. [Explains and illustrates the principles of directness, simplicity, clarity, and accuracy in designing pie, bar, column, curve, and surface charts.]

MCLUHAN, MARSHALL. *Understanding Media: The Extensions of Man.* New York: McGraw-Hill Book Company, 1965. [Discusses how electronic media and the new technology have influenced the sending and receiving of information.]

TUCKER, S. MARION. *Public Speaking for Technical Men.* New York: McGraw-Hill Book Company, Inc., 1939. [Communicating to an audience, platform manners and techniques, using the voice, organizing a speech, effective words and sentences.]

WEISS, HAROLD, and J. B. MCGRATH, JR. *Technical Speaking: Oral Communication for Engineers, Scientists, and Technical Personnel.* New York: McGraw-Hill Book Company, Inc., 1963. [Informal conversation, group situations, and formal speech. Plentiful examples of speaking situations in which technical people often find themselves.]

WILCOX, ROGER P. *Oral Reporting in Business and Industry.* Englewood Cliffs, New Jersey: Prentice-Hall, Inc., 1967. [Practical advice based on communication theory and on speaking situations at General Motors. Suggestions on developing ideas, using visual and audio aids, and on conducting question periods.]

ZELKO, HAROLD P., and FRANK E. X. DANCE. *Business and Professional Speech Communication.* New York: Holt, Rinehart, and Winston, Inc., 1965. [Communicating in a variety of situations: speechmaking, interviewing, counseling, conferences, selling, etc.]

ARTICLES AND PAPERS

CARLIN, THOMAS W. "How to Hold an Audience." *Chemical Engineering,* 72:90, 93-94 (February 1, 1965). [Methods of organizing and delivering a speech to hold an audience.]

CONNOLLY, JAMES E. "The Training of the Technical Speaker," Paper E-1, in *Proceedings of the Fifteenth International Technical Communications Conference.* Papers presented at the Society of Technical Writers and Publishers Convention, May 8-11, 1968, Los Angeles, California. [Describes the need for skill in orally communicating technical information; recommends that technical speakers be familiar with the theoretical and practical concepts of verbal presentation as well as the human elements of communication; and suggests that perhaps industries rather than colleges are doing the most effective job of training technical speakers.]

CRUM, ROY W. "Technical Tedium—or Otherwise." *Civil Engineering*, 31:46-47 (September 1961). [A comparison-contrast between a badly delivered and a well-delivered paper.]

ESTRIN, HERMAN A. "Speech in the Curriculum for Scientific and Technical Students." Paper presented at the convention of the National Council of Teachers of English, Cleveland, Ohio, November 27, 1964. [Discusses the results of a questionnaire survey concerning the content, philosophy, and techniques of speech courses offered to technical students in colleges and universities.]

HAND, HARRY E. "Technical Speech: A Need for Teaching and Research." *IEEE Transactions on Engineering Writing and Speech*, EWS-10:48-51 (December 1967). [Proposes research into matters of audience, delivery, and audiovisual aids that might provide valuable information about successful technical speaking.]

HAND, HARRY E. "Technical Speech—Orphan of the Streets?" in *Spinoff: Practical Uses of Communication Research*. Papers presented at a Joint Regional Meeting of the American Business Writing Association and the Society of Technical Writers and Publishers, Cincinnati, Ohio April 8, 1967. [Urges the teaching of technical speech in colleges and universities and research into several areas of technical speaking.]

HASKITT, HAROLD O., JR. "What Industry Is Doing to Help Improve Oral Presentations—A Case in Point," Paper E-2, in *Proceedings of the Fifteenth International Technical Com-*

munications Conference. Papers presented at the Society of Technical Writers and Publishers Convention, May 8-11, 1968, Los Angeles, California. [Describes the content and techniques of speech courses taught to undergraduate students, managers, engineers, and sales people at General Motors Institute and in the Continuing Education Programs of General Motors.]

HEINMILLER, PAUL R. "Should You Make That Speech?" *Product Engineering, 32*: 52-53 (May 29, 1961). [Guideposts to help the technical man in deciding whether to accept or reject a speaking invitation.]

"How to Turn Technical People into Speakers." *Sales Management (Part II), 89*:36-38 (July 20, 1962). [Preparing and delivering a talk for a convention audience.]

KRAMER, HARRY P., and MARSHA M. MYERS. "So You're Going to Give a Paper." *Journal Water Pollution Control Federation, 35:* 43-56 (January 1963). [Preparing, outlining, and writing a speech; words and vocabulary; voice, pitch, pace, enunciation; effective visual communication. Examples, illustrations, references.]

NELSON, ROY C. "The Humanity of Speech," in *Proceedings of the 1961 Institute in Technical and Industrial Communications,* ed. by Herman M. Weisman. Fort Collins, Colorado: Institute in Technical and Industrial Communications, Colorado State University, 1961, pp. 55-59. [Develops the thesis that speech is more than communication: it is a vital part of human behavior and an important expression of the personality.]

ROBERTS, ORVILLE, JR. "Speaking Your Way to Success." *Petroleum Engineer for Management, 32*:A34-A36 (May

1960). [Selecting and developing a topic to hold an audience.]

SCHREIBER, FLORA RHETA. "How to Speak Better." *Science Digest*, *51*:13-18 (March 1962). [Developing and controlling the voice for effective speaking qualities such as force, rate, pitch, quality, breath control, etc.]

TANGERMAN, E. J. "7 Steps to Better Oral Reporting." *Product Engineering*, *36*:94 (July 19, 1965); 69 (August 2, 1965); 104 (August 16, 1965); 68 (August 30, 1965); 144 (September 13, 1965); 71 (September 27, 1965); 125 (October 11, 1965). [Brief, to-the-point coverage of several topics: making notes and outlines; organization; preparing the spoken version of a speech; delivery and visual aids; preparing for the audience; chairing technical panels, committees, and meetings.]

THOMPSON, WARREN C. "Technical Speech for Logistics Managers," Paper E-3, in *Proceedings of the Fifteenth International Technical Communications Conference*. Papers presented at the Society of Technical Writers and Publishers Convention, May 8-11, 1968, Los Angeles, California. [Describes speech training given students at the School of Systems and Logistics, Air Force Institute of Technology. The training course tries to simulate the circumstances actually faced by logistics officers in high staff positions.]

TUPES, ERNEST C., WALTER R. BORG, and A. CARP. "Relationships Between an Impromptu Speech and Criteria of Military Success." *Personnel Psychology*, *11*:383-391 (Autumn 1958). [Describes a research project conducted by the U.S. Air Force in which impromptu speaking was used as a means of assessing the ability of Air Force Officer Candidates. The study indicated a relationship between speech scores and other measurements of ability such as verbal fluency, intelligence, and social maturity.]

WIKSELL, MILTON J. "Is Your Audience With You?" *The Management Review*, *49:*16-20 (July 1960). [Capturing the attention of an audience and holding it.]

WILLIAMSON, MERRITT A. "Preparing a Paper for Delivery." *Research/Development*, *16:*56, 61 (November 1965). [Preparing and reading a paper especially designed for oral delivery.]

ZELKO, HAROLD P. "How to Be a Better Speaker." *Nation's Business*, *53:*88, 90, 93, 94, 96 (Apr. 1965). [Attacks five big myths about good speech-making and offers positive alternatives.]

APPENDIX C

Checklist for preparing and giving a technical speech

ANALYZING THE AUDIENCE

1. Analyze the audience for their knowledge and experience in technical matters. An audience listening to a technical presentation may consist of fellow specialists, specialists in another technical field, technical managers or decision makers (sometimes uninformed about technical matters), or lay people. An electrical engineer explaining the latest developments in the design and manufacture of transistors would include and stress different information for audiences of electrical engineers, chemists, technical managers, or Rotarians.

2. Analyze the audience for their particular interest in the subject and their need to know the information. An audience of technical managers may not want or need to hear about the physics of transistors in a speech describing the latest techniques for manufacturing transistors.

3. Analyze the audience for their attitudes toward the subject and toward the speaker, and for any fixed beliefs that

they may hold. Reliability engineers may be unsympathetic toward psychologists and behavioral research—unless the importance or relation to their field can be demonstrated.

DETERMINING THE PURPOSE OF THE SPEECH

4. Determine the general purpose of the talk. Is its purpose to inform, to convince, or both?

5. Determine the specific purpose or objective of the talk. Write it down in one or two sentences. *Examples:* (1) The purpose of my speech on designing the wings for a new aircraft is to explain why and how the wings were designed (informative). *OR* (2) The purpose of my speech on designing the wings for a new aircraft is to convince the audience that this design should be used in all future aircraft (persuasive). *OR* (3) A combination of both (1) and (2), informative plus persuasive.

SELECTING AND ORGANIZING THE DATA

6. Select data and information which suits the audience, the purpose of the speech, the situation, and the time limits imposed.

7. Guided by the statement of exact purpose, prepare a sentence outline of the speech. Outlining helps to develop ideas logically and concretely. The outline can be put on 3x5 cards for facilitating extemporaneous delivery.

8. Write out the whole speech if it is to be read from a manuscript. Even if the speech is not read from a manuscript, writing out the speech helps to completely develop all ideas.

9. Check the introduction of the speech to make sure that it states the following information: (1) subject and purpose of the speech; (2) scope of the speech, that is, what will be covered, and what will not be covered; (3) your plan of developing the speech; and (4) importance and application of the information (a motivating device).

10. Check the body of the speech to make sure that it explains, clarifies, develops, and emphasizes principal points. The following rhetorical devices can aid in clarifying information: (1) repetition of important points, preferably in varied ways; (2) transitions which sum up long sections of statistics, formulas, graphic aids, etc., and transitions which set the stage for the next important point to be covered; (3) definition and description of special or unfamiliar terms, mechanisms, and processes; (4) comparison and contrast between new concepts and old concepts, and between the abstract and the concrete; and (5) examples and illustrations of new and abstract ideas.

11. Check the closing of the speech to make sure that it emphasizes important points. Closings usually summarize vital information, state conclusions, or offer recommendations.

12. Plan and prepare suitable audiovisual aids (charts, blackboards, slides, handouts, films, models, tapes, etc.) if they are needed in presenting data and equations, showing relationships (tables and graphs), illustrating forms and shapes, reinforcing lists and conclusions, etc. People learn faster through the eyes than the ears, and they remember more if they both hear *and* see.

13. In planning the use of audiovisual aids, remember that they should be (1) limited in number; (2) relevant to the topic and helpful to understanding (not a parade of unneces-

sary props competing for the attention of the audience); (3) easy to comprehend (simply designed, stripped to essentials, adequately labeled); (4) limited to one idea per display; (5) pictorial rather than verbal whenever possible; (6) presented precisely at the moment needed (because earlier distracting and later ineffective); (7) removed immediately after discussion to prevent distraction; (8) visible to everyone; (9) thoroughly discussed by the speaker; and (10) grouped in the body of the talk as a unit to prevent on-and-off-again interruptions.

PRACTICING THE SPEECH

14. Practice delivering the speech *extemporaneously*. Do not memorize it, but rehearse it several times, speaking from an outline and notes on 3x5 cards. The advantages of extemporaneous delivery are naturalness, spontaneity, and flexibility. Dry run the speech before a friend who matches the audience profile, or with a tape recorder. Criticism, even your own, can be helpful.

15. If the speech is to be read from a manuscript, for example at a professional meeting where detailed and sophisticated knowledge often is delivered in speaker-packages, be sure to read the manuscript slowly, carefully, and audibly—pausing before and after important points, stressing important words, and looking at the audience as much as possible. And above all, remember that a manuscript designed for listeners is not the same as a manuscript for readers. Slowly, simply, and carefully develop the message, often repeating important points.

16. Pay attention to the choice of words, both in extemporaneous and manuscript speaking. The accuracy of tech-

nical words must not be sacrificed, but new or difficult terms can be defined. Use simple, familiar, concrete terms whenever possible. Avoid jargon (big words for familiar but yet precise words, and abstract words for concrete words). Avoid gobbledygook (jargon and extra words that do not add to the meaning). Avoid technical slang or shoptalk which may be familiar to one group but completely unfamiliar to another group.

17. Strive for platform poise. The voice should be conversational, and gestures and mannerisms natural. Posture should be dignified but relaxed. Use as much eye contact as possible so that listeners feel a sense of direct communication.

18. Do not worry about nervousness. It is natural. It can be alleviated by reading the opening or closing, by thoroughly knowing and preparing the topic, and by practicing the speech in a room which matches the physical characteristics of the actual location.

APPENDIX D

Checklist for planning and conducting a committee conference

THE COMMITTEE CHAIRMAN

1. Learn as much as you can about the topic to be discussed or the problem to be solved. Use books, newspapers, periodicals, reports, and qualified authorities to gather information and facts. You do not need to be an authority on the topic or problem, but you should be acquainted with it.

2. Prepare a tentative agenda or a plan of discussion. Try to divide the topic into appropriate sub-topics.

3. Prepare a motivating introduction which explains why the topic or problem needs attention and which encourages the participation of the group.

4. Present an agenda for the consideration of the group, and inform them of the probable time limits for the immediate session. Allow the group to make changes, additions, or deletions to the agenda if they think their changes helpful. Do not become bogged down in debating fine points or details in the agenda.

5. Prepare one or two carefully thought out questions which can be used to get the discussion started off on the right track.

6. If the group wanders from the agenda or agreed on plan, inform them, and try to get them to return to the agenda. If they insist on following a new path of discussion, be sure they realize that they have started on a new track.

7. Ask the recorder or secretary of the group to present a summary of the group's thinking whenever necessary or helpful. These situations usually occur when there is confusion about what has been covered, said, or agreed on; and when the group has finished one item on the agenda and is ready to move on to the next. The chairman himself should be ready to present a final summary at the end of the discussion.

8. Give members of the group a chance to recommend corrections or additions to summaries. All summaries must be an accurate account of what the group has actively said or accomplished.

9. If the group strays or bogs down, remind them of the time limitations that were announced at the start of the group discussion. Your tone should encourage them to press on, but should not make them feel nervous or anxious.

10. Because the advantage of a group discussion is to pool the ideas of many individuals, encourage all members of the group to contribute to the discussion. Do not let a few people dominate the discussion and impose their thinking on the group.

THE COMMITTEE RECORDER

1. Keep a record of the following information: major points discussed by the group; points on which the group agreed

and disagreed; points which were never clarified or resolved; points merely mentioned but not discussed.

2. If called on by the chairman, be ready to make an on-the-spot report of what has been discussed or agreed on. Be ready to give a final summary if needed.

3. Do not editorialize or add your own views to the record. Your major job is to report objectively the major points discussed and decided upon. You should ask members of the group to amend the report if they believe that it does not accurately reflect the discussion.

4. Do not feel it necessary to report every minor point or every member's contribution. It is not necessary to attach names to what was said unless you think that a minority view or a key disagreement needs to be pinpointed.

5. Keep a concise but sufficiently clear record so that a written report of the discussion can be prepared if needed.

6. Remember that your efficiency in identifying, recording, and reporting essential items helps to insure a successful discussion.

COMMITTEE MEMBERS

1. Learn all you can about the topic to be discussed or the problem to be solved. Do not be satisfied with what you may already know. The success of the discussion depends on the contributions of all members.

2. Pay attention to the introductions, comments, and summaries offered by the committee leader or the recorder.

3. Try to build on the contributions of each member. Do not automatically reject an idea until it has had a chance to be considered.

4. Distinguish between facts and opinions. Pinpoint the authorities or references you use. If you refer to personal experiences, be sure they are relevant to the point being discussed.

5. Define your terms, and if necessary, ask others to do the same. Do not rely on emotional appeals, hasty generalizations, and figurative analogies to establish your points.

6. Do not monopolize the discussion or stretch out small points. Give others a chance to participate.

7. Do not sidetrack the discussion by engaging in personal or heated arguments. Factual matters seldom require heated arguments. On matters of opinion, ask some of the other group members how they feel about the point being discussed.

8. Be ready to contribute, explain, and defend your ideas. If you find that you are wrong, be honest and gracious enough to change your views.

9. If you are particularly well informed on a point or have special knowledge, be ready to aid the leader and the group when called upon.

10. Remember that you can often help other group members to express themselves by paraphrasing or summarizing their contributions.

Index

Abstracts, 26
Amplifier
  arranging for, 141
  when not necessary, 51
Analogies, effective use of, 24-25
Anecdotes, use of, 32, 150
Apologies, effect on audience, 120
Audience
  adapting subject to, 22, 161
  aim toward average, 54-55
  analyzing the, 265-266
  arousing interest of, 69-70
  evaluate the, 25 43, 133
  importance of, 20-21
  non-technical, addressing the, 28-34
  rules for handling, 120-121
  secondary, importance of, 170-171
  See also Props; Reading manuscripts, delivery techniques; Speeches, factors for failure of; Speeches, factors for successful; Voice
Audience levels, 22
Audiovisual aids, 175, 267-268
  See also Visual aids
Automation box, 87

Blackboard
  advantage over slides, 56
  as a lecture prop, 86, 143
  techniques for good use of, 55-56, 118, 119
Body of speech, 31-32, 96-97

Chairman, duties of
  checklist for, 271-272
  in committee meetings, 139, 141
  in emergencies, 144-145
  in group thinking, 140
  in making physical arrangements, 140-141
  in panel discussions, 139, 141
  in personal care of speaker, 143-144

  in planning ahead, 138
  in technical meetings, 142-145
Charts, *see* Visual aids
Color, *see* Slides, use of color in
Committee meetings
  duties of members, 273-274
  duties of recorder, 272-273
  duties of vice-chairman or secretary, 141
  system for developing information for, 244-245
  See also Chairman, duties of
Concluding a speech, 32-33, 53, 97, 106-107, 108, 121, 267
Conclusions, in special reports, 163

Delivery of speeches, factors for effective, 34, 51-60, 98-100, 109, 126
  See also Platform poise; Reading manuscripts
Demonstrations
  implementing for closed circuit television, 218-228
  using in talks, 68, 119
Diagrams, *see* Visual aids

Enthusiasm, role of, in speeches, 100-101
Experiments, presentation of, 68-69
Extemporaneous speeches, *see* Speeches, types of
Eye contact with audience, 100

Fear, 9-10
Flow diagrams, presenting slides of, 202-205
Formulae, presentation of, 201

Gestures, 48, 119
Graphic devices, suitability of, 189-190
Graphs, *see* Visual aids
Group thinking, 140, 271-272
Guest speakers, handling, 143-145

Handouts, 162-163

Impromptu speeches, *see* Speeches, types of
Introduction
 of speakers, 148-154
 of speech, *see* Opening a speech

Jargon, 57, 58, 115-116, 269
Jokes, use of, 70

Language, *see* Jargon; Speeches, language considerations in
lectern, 132, 133
Lecturers, courteous treatment of, 71-72
Lectures
 and scripts for publication, 129
 order of material for, 69-70
 reading of, arguments against, 66-67, 83, 90-93, 128-129
 rules for successful, 64-68
 timing of, 70-71
 using demonstrations with, 68
 using slides with, 68
Lighting, *see* Slides, lighting when showing

Magnetic board, use of, 68
Manuscripts, *see* Reading manuscripts
Mathematical formulae, making slides for, 201-202
Meetings, *see* Chairman, duties of; Committee meetings
Memorizing speeches, 13, 52, 115
Microphone
 and good speech and voice techniques, 230-231, 235-237
 characteristics of, 233-235
 lapel type, use in demonstrations, 192
 testing before meetings, 143
Mirror, practice before, 133
Monitors, using in CCTV, 221

Nervousness, to overcome, 117, 269

Obstacles to effective speaking, 9-10
Opening a speech, 30-31, 32, 67, 97, 106-107, 115, 127, 148-154, 267
Opinion Research Corporation survey, 166-172
Oral communication
 principles of, 124-129
 versus written, 103-111
Oral manuscripts, *see* Reading manuscripts
Oral report, checklist of parts for, 159
Organization of speeches, *see* Speeches, organization of
Outline, model, 107-108
Outlining of speeches, *see* Speeches, outlining of
Overhead projector, *see* Projector
Overlay technique, 242

Panel discussions, 139, 140-141
Payment of speakers, 144
Personal opinions, in special report, 163
Photography, use of color for slides, 192
Pictographs, for slides, *see* Visual aids
Pie diagrams for slides, *see* Visual aids
Platform poise, 8-15
 See also Reading manuscripts; Speeches, factors for failure; Speeches, factors for making successful; Speeches, rehearsing
Pointer
 using with screen, 118-119
 using with slides, 192
Poise, *see* Platform poise
Polaroid materials, animated effects with, 207
Posture, 117
Presents to speakers, 144
Press, members of, 71-72
Private languages, 42, 49, 57-58
Projector
 advanced techniques with, 207
 overhead, use of, 240-241, 243-244
 with polaroid materials, 207
Prompting words, 115
Props
 arranging for, 143
 as interest arousers, 31
 automation box, 87
 handouts, 162-163
 magnetic board, 68
 monitors, 221
 polaroid materials, 207
 signal devices for slides, 205
 wide-screen projection, 207

INDEX 277

See also Amplifiers; Blackboard; Demonstrations; Microphone; Pointer; Projector; Screen; Slides; Transparencies; Visual aids
Public address systems, see Microphones
Purpose of talks, see Speeches, purpose of
Push button, for showing slides, 205

Reading manuscripts
  acceptable occasions for, 78
  advantages of, 80-82
  arguments pro and con, 77-86
  delivery techniques, 34, 53, 79-82, 99-100, 115, 132-135
  disadvantages of, 84-85, 90-93, 177, 178
  goals of, 131-132
  student reactions to, 83
  versus extemporaneous delivery, 249-255
  versus memorizing, 52
  See also Lectures, reading of; Oral communication
Rehearsing a speech, see Speeches, rehearsing
Repetition, need for, in speeches, 38-39
Reports, making effective, 158-163
Reprints, effective use of, 170-171
Revelation technique, 242

Scientific communication, checklist for, 25-26
Scientific papers, checklist for presentation of, 113-121
Screen, use of, with pointer, 118-119
Secretary, duties of, 141
Seven key words, 149
Shock, as speaking device, 30-31
Signal devices, for slides, 205
Simplicity, checklist for, 122
Singing lessons, as an aid to speech, 236-237
Slides
  bridging, 216
  effective use of, 56, 68, 80, 114, 125-127, 129, 162, 176-179, 181-193, 211-216
  flow diagrams shown on, 202-203
  for technical talks, 26, 41, 196-207
  graphs shown on, 200-201
  formulae shown on, 201-202
  how to handle, 115
  lettering on, 187-188, 190-191, 197, 202
  lighting when showing, 177, 179, 192, 193, 205, 216
  maintaining continuity when showing, 205
  of mathematical formulae, 201-202
  rules for preparing, 197
  tables shown on, 198-200
  techniques for showing, 205-206
  timing, 186, 205-206
  use of color in, 192, 198, 206-207
  See also Transparencies; Visual aids
Snide remarks, effect on audience, 120
Speakers
  how to get invitations, 169
  making arrangements for visiting, 142-144
  overexposure of, 168
  stand-in, 144-145
  See also Audiences; Platform poise; Speeches; Voice
Speaking, public, four factors in, 107
  See also Microphone; Platform poise; Reading manuscripts
Speaking invitations, 168-169
Speech, components of good, 231-233
Speeches
  body, 31-32, 96-97
  classical errors in, 171-172
  factors in failure of, 171-173, 177, 181-183
  factors in making successful, 37-39, 47-48, 51-58, 64-65, 95-97, 100-101, 113-121, 127, 148, 169-170, 178-179
  language considerations in, 18-20, 42, 57, 58, 79, 98, 109, 116, 172, 268-269
  memorizing, 13, 52, 115
  organizing, 33-34, 39-43, 65, 75, 96-97, 159-160, 266-268
  outlining, 33-34, 39-40, 107
  principles of scientific communication, 25-26
  purpose of, 25, 62-65, 84, 86, 166-167, 266

278 INDEX

reading technique, checklist for, 132-134
rehearsing, 13-14, 99-100, 109-110, 124-125, 268-269
style factors for, 58-60, 98, 105, 171-173
timing of, 53-54, 70-71, 77, 109, 124, 125
titles for, 29
types of: extemporaneous, 96, 125, 147-155, 268-269; for non-technical audience, 28-35; introductory, 148-154; oral report, 158-164; technical, see Technical talk; "thank you," 154-156
use of jargon in, 57, 58, 115-116
written for executives, 169-170
See also Concluding a speech; Delivery of speeches; Lectures; Opening a speech; Props; Reading manuscripts
Speech making, checklist for successful, 47-48
practices common to leader companies, 168-173
Speech technique, for microphone, 230-237
Stories, use of, 32
Style, 58-59
Surveys of educational needs for public speaking, 166-168

Tables, see Visual aids
Talk, definition of, 63-65
See also Speeches
Tape recordings, for rehearsing speeches, 99-100, 109
Technical talk, checklist for preparing and giving, 265-269
common types of sequence for, 106
criterion of success for, 47
guides for preparing, 39-43
main requirement for, 39
See also Reading manuscripts; Speeches
Technical terms, see Jargon
Television, closed circuit
arranging facilities, 219-220
instrumentation, 223-224
monitors, 221

oscillator efficiency, 227
planning the presentation, 221
projection apparatus, 222
test circuit, 224-226
"Thank you" speeches, checklist of material for, 154-156
Timing
of slides, 186, 204-206
of speech, 53-54, 70-71, 109, 124, 125
Titles for talks, 29
Transparencies
for blueprints, 243
for overhead projector, 240-241
overlay technique, 242
See also Slides

Vice-chairman, duties of, 141
Visual aids
charts: color in, 162, 206; designing, 162, 191; effective use of, 68, 105, 186, 192, 196, 211-214
diagrams; block versus photograph, 105; flow, for slides, 202-204; pie, for slides, 188, 189; use of, with blackboard, 118
effective use of, 41-42, 86, 100, 163, 175, 211-216, 243-245, 267-268
flow diagrams, presenting slides of, 202-205
graphs: color in, 206-207; designing, 187-190, 197, 200; effective use of, 68, 105, 186, 192, 196, 211-214
pictographs, for slides, 188, 189
tables: avoid use of, 197; designing, 190-191, 198-199; effective use of, 192; use of color in, 206
Visual Communication System, 240-243
See also Slides
Visual Communication System, 240-245
Voice
trick for projecting, 51-52
test loudness of, 125
See also Reading manuscripts; Speeches, rehearsing; Speech technique

Whiffle's syndrome, 184-185